To Bobbie

with deep appreciation
from Joan & Larry Clarke
7/10/1981

THE
FINELY FITTED YACHT

Ferenc Maté

ILLUSTRATED BY

Candace Maté

ALBATROSS PUBLISHING HOUSE

box 33766   vancouver bc   canada   V6J 4L6

Other Books
By

Ferenc Maté

"FROM A BARE HULL"
An Encyclopedia of Boatbuilding

"WATERHOUSES"
Houseboats and Floating Homes

THE
FINELY FITTED YACHT

BY

Ferenc Maté

ILLUSTRATED BY

Candace Maté

PHOTOGRAPHED BY THE AUTHOR.

Volume I Interior

137 illustrations
62 photographs

DISTRIBUTED IN THE U.S. BY W.W. NORTON
500 FIFTH AVENUE, NEW YORK

To Susan and Eric Hiscock,
for their inspiration

Philosophically

There is little joy in creating junk. Boats live a long time and so do people, and so does the spark of pride in a lovingly crafted piece of wood or canvas. Have patience, enjoy every step. You may never get the chance to do it again.

Specifically

Start big. Begin with the project that requires the largest piece of material and you'll definitely be safe, for then if you miscut or misdrill or misthink, you can always pretend that you were actually working on the next size down object in the first place, and you wanted a smaller piece of whatever anyway, and you're not *really* as big-a-stupid as the puzzled onlookers think you are.

Of course, there are limits. If you began with a piece for the boom gallows, and ended up with eight pounds of teak toothpicks, stop and reflect, then yank out a chunk of old line, and just tie the bloody boom to the backstay. . . . Stupid.

Generally

I'm not familiar with every skylight, dinghy chock or awning in the whole wide world. As a matter of fact, I have an acquaintance with only a few of each, so by no means does this book contain *the ultimates*. But all things in it have been tested, or built, or at least dreamt about thoroughly, and within those limits they all worked. . . . More or less.

Thankfully

Our thanks to the many kind people, from Antigua to Hawaii, whose yachts we invaded with cameras and notebooks and tape measures.

Our gratitude to Jean Koefed of Charles Scribner's Sons and Eric Swenson of W.W. Norton, and the gracious people at Princeton Tools, Detco Marine, Garrett Wade Company, Leichtung Tools, The Adjustable Clamp Company, Faire Harbour Ltd. and Spyglass Catalogue for their help and photographs.

TABLE OF CONTENTS

SECTION I: GALLEY

SECTION II: HEAD

SECTION III: CHART TABLE AND NAVIGATION

SECTION IV: SALON

SECTION V: LAMPS AND STOVES

SECTION VI: ENGINE ROOM

SECTION VII: STOWAGE

SECTION VIII: BIBELOTS

galley

SINK BOARD WITH DRAIN TRAY

Since chopping boards are rather a pain to stow aboard a yacht at the best of times, perhaps the best solution is to have one fitted over the sink where it: a) will provide extra counter space, and b) can be stowed when the sink is not in use. For chopping board construction, see section under that name. One special caution should be taken, however; only long strips of wood should be used for this operation, since the board will be supported only at its edges, unlike a standard board which is evenly supported on a counter top.

So make your chopping board as you wish, leaving a 1″ overhang all around the sink. Next, you'll have to devise a way to keep it from sliding about. Two methods can be used: a) for 1″ or thinner boards, run an open corner frame of cleat stock around the bottom of the board, so it will fit reasonably tightly into the sink. I mentioned open corners, for most sinks have theirs generously radiused, and the effort spent trying to get your cleat stock modified to accommodate that radius would be totally wasted, and b) for 1½″ or thicker boards, a more difficult, but aesthetically pleasing, job can be done by rabbeting (with two cuts of the table saw) a 3/4″ × 1″ rabbet into the lower edges, so part of the board will slip into the sink and act as its own restrainer. Once the cutting has been done, you will have to rasp away the corners to suit the radius of the sink, but this should pose no more than ten minute's work. It may behoove you to rasp a dimple into the leftover lower edge on all four sides, so a finger can slip under the board for lifting. Of course, if you don't mind stripping your fingernails from your fingertips, don't bother with this detail.

The acutely aware will recognize the need to relocate the board when the sink is to be used. The best place, of course, is right next to the sink, upside down, where it can be used as a drainboard for dishes. To make this drainboard leak-proof in the simplest way possible, trot down to your corner supermarket or hardware store and purchase a little plastic container (the largest that will slip into the sink upside down), then trot home and attach it with epoxy or plastic container attacher to the bottom of your chopping board.

Voilà. A perfect little drain tray and an impeccable bath tub for midgets.

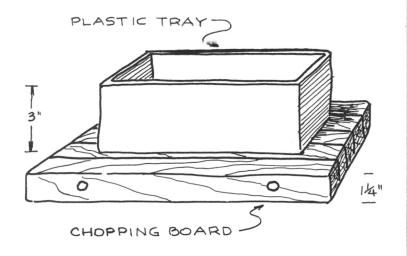

PLASTIC TRAY

3"

1¼"

CHOPPING BOARD

SINK BOARD WITH DRAIN TRAY

COOKWARE STOWAGE

I think it of vital importance that the ship's cook be kept as happy and complacent as possible, for few things are less appetizing than a bitchy cook stirring sock-stew in his cauldron. To this end, all cooking gear should be exposed and readily accessible, but *noise free*. An attempt should be made to purchase a set of cookware with similar size holes in the handles to eliminate the need for reaming and other such nonsensical modifications. When all possible gear has been gathered (including the fine little measuring pots), determine the amount of space you will need for the whole show, and mark in the locations for the 1/4" dowels to be used as hooks. These will be inserted as in the "Pot Rack." One difference here is that no more than 3/4" of dowel can be allowed to protrude, for any more length will not allow the utensils (limited in movement by the fixed leather strapping) to slip over the long pegs and into place.

Be sure to take the same precautions as mentioned in the "Pot Rack" section regarding thin bulkheads and cabinsides. If the cabinside is the only resort, and it is made of unreinforced ultra-thin fiberglass, cut a length of 1" × 3/8" by whatever length stock, insert and glue the dowels into it, and then epoxy that to the cabinside.

Next, cut a length of 1" wide leather strapping, about one and a half times the length of the row of utensils. A nice old leather belt will do just fine here. Tack one end down past the first utensil, loop it somewhat loosely over it, then tack down, and so on. If you have a thin cabinside, cut another piece of stock, same width and length you need to mount the pegs, epoxy it to the cabinside, and drive your tacks into this. Be sure you place your strapping no lower than 4" from the top of the handle, or you will require entirely too much unobstructed space below your tools for maneuvering.

If all this gleaming hardware doesn't make cooky happy, throw the bugger overboard.

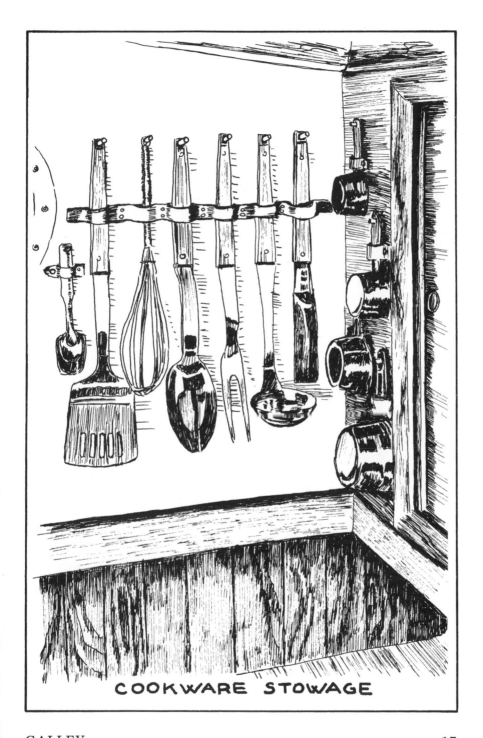

COOKWARE STOWAGE

CUTLERY RACK

No proper yacht would have loose cutlery beating itself to death in a drawer. Drawer space is a precious commodity in any galley and should be saved to store ugly things like spatulas and rubber bands. Tasteful eating tools should have a rack of their own where they will be: a) removable with one hand, and b) tight and quiet. This rack should be of modest size. Contemplating something like grandma's silver set case with each fork in its own velvet nook is an absurdity. Cutlery for six need not have a case larger than $7'' \times 7'' \times 3\frac{1}{2}''$ if the cutlery is sensibly selected, that is, one with modest curvature. One-quarter-inch solid stock should be used for all sides and interior baffles, while a single piece of $1\frac{1}{2}''$ stock $1/2''$ narrower than the exterior width of the rack will do for knife stowage.

The inside compartmentalization should involve four spaces plus the knife block: $1\frac{1}{2}''$ for six spoons, $1\frac{1}{4}''$ for six teaspoons, $1\frac{1}{4}''$ for salad forks, and $1\frac{1}{2}''$ for dinner forks. The remaining width will be consumed by the baffles and the two sides. The $1\frac{1}{2}''$ stock for the knives should have slits cut on $3/4''$ centres. Mark slits wide enough to house the knife blades and part of the handles as well. In a $7''$ high rack, you should have no difficulty immersing at least $3/4$ of the average knife.

Since delicate $1/4''$ stock is being used, it would be prudent to let in and glue all the pieces instead of using brass tacks or screws and plugs. Again, as in all box construction, the face should completely cover the edges of the sides. You will find it advantageous to designate the two central compartments for the short tools (salad forks and teaspoons), and then cut a semi-circular piece out of the face to allow finger access to these mostly submersed pieces. The bottom piece must have at least one drain hole per compartment to facilitate cleaning.

Mount it in any available area in the galley, making sure adequate space exists above for smooth removal, especially of the long knives. We made the mistake of mounting ours too close to our brass chronometer and have suffered numerous hairline scratches on the brass ring as a consequence.

If mounting screws can be inserted from behind, by all means attempt it, for it will save marring the teak face with plugs.

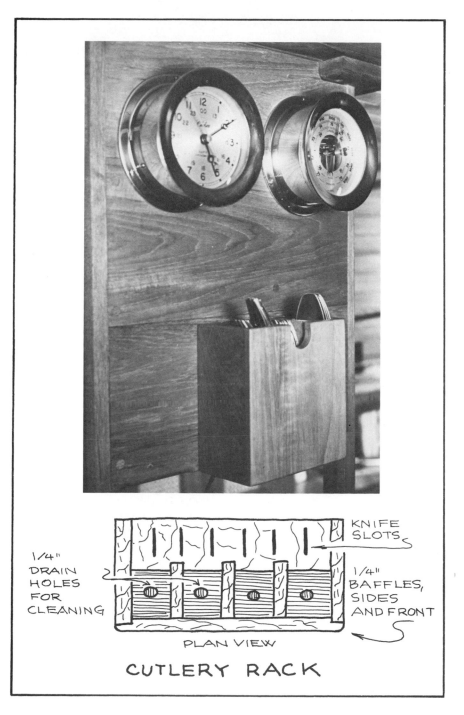

KNIFE
SLOTS

1/4"
DRAIN
HOLES
FOR
CLEANING

1/4"
BAFFLES,
SIDES
AND FRONT

PLAN VIEW

CUTLERY RACK

SPICE RACK

Any vessel used even only a few weeks a year, should have its own spices and its own spice rack. Hauling spices back and forth from house to boat and back again is usually self-defeating, for not only will you forget the spice you need the most, but the odd shapes and sizes of the containers will create a noisy and unsightly mess in galley lockers.

Once the number of spices required has been decided upon, a set of containers must be found. Tin cans are out of the question: they rust within weeks. Honed out wood containers are nice, but few woods are transparent and great amounts of time will be spent label reading — hardly a pleasant occupation in a seaway. That leaves glass spice jars. They can be obtained of heavy glass, with fine plastic lined stoppers, at the reasonable cost of fifty cents each, unfortunately full only of air. Full of spices of various colors and texture, they are extremely appetizing. The jars are usually 1½″ in diameter and 4″ in height, including the stopper. A marvelously simple and appealing rack can be constructed out of four pieces of wood and a piece of heavy fishing line.

Determine the length of the rack by the number of jars you will need, and rip a piece of 13/16″ stock to that length by a 2½″ width. Rip another piece to the same length, but a 3½″ width. This piece will be the back of the rack and will allow 1/2″ of the jars stoppers to protrude for easy handling. Cut the end pieces to a 2½″ width by a 4¼″ height, cutting off the top corners, or radiusing them, to reduce visual severity and awkwardness. Glue and screw the back piece onto the shelf. With an extremely fine drill bit, drill a hole in one end piece about 1/4″ in from the face and 2½″ from the bottom. Countersink this very slightly on the outside with a slightly larger drill bit. For the other end piece, secure a tuning peg from a ukulele and drill a hole in the end piece the size of its shank. Fix the end piece in place with glue and screws. Next, fetch a length of heavy gauge fishing line and tie a tidy knot in one end, then thread it through the small hole of one end piece and out the shank hole (via a perpendicularly drilled hole) of the other end piece. Wrap a few turns of line onto the tuning peg, make fast, and cut off the rest. Insert the peg in the hole and twist to a tune of G Major. Secure the rack to a bulkhead or cabinet with three staggered screws. Pop the little jars in place. Lovely.

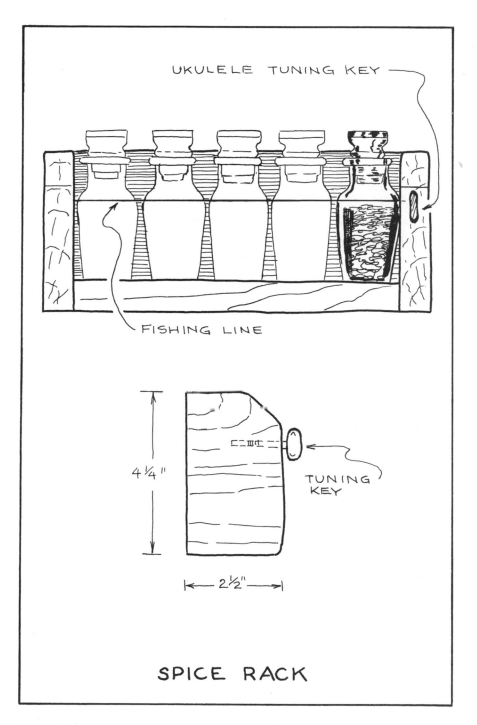

UKULELE TUNING KEY

FISHING LINE

4 1/4 "

TUNING KEY

2 1/2 "

SPICE RACK

PAPER TOWEL RACK

Possibly no other expendable item is expended in as great a quantity as paper towels. Now, it is quite probable that I'm measurably neurotic who's constantly cleaning, wiping, dusting and mopping, but even if one was only half as neurotic as I, using merely half the amount of towels, the quantity would still be quite astounding. For this reason, I feel paper towels require a well thought out, well located holder of their own. The holders fall into two general varieties: exposed and discreet.

Exposed

These are close kin to the store-bought plastic ones, but infinitely more decorative. Cut 3/4″ stock to a roughly 4″ × 4″ piece, drastically radiusing the front corners. Bullnose all but the back edges. Cut a piece of 1/2″ dowel to a length of 13″ (most paper towels come in 11″ rolls). In the centre of the radiused front, drill a 5/8″ hole to a depth of 3/8″. On the inside of the other piece rout a 1/2″ wide and 3/8″ deep reverse "J". See diagram. This will enable you to have the two end pieces fixed, and have fresh rolls easily dropped in from the top with the dowel the only moving part. Attaching the towel rack can be performed at this stage, if the bulkhead, cabinet, or whatever has access from the rear. You can drill pilot holes from the front, positioning your two end pieces in place, and drill and screw from the back. If no rear access exists, a back will have to be made of 1/4″ solid wood onto which the ends can be mounted, then this, in turn, can be screwed to bulkhead, etc. It seems the three major towel consuming centres are the galley, the engine room, and the cockpit, therefore, location near the companionway would be desirable.

Discreet

For those who do not find a roll of paper particularly decorative, a simple dispenser type system exists. This involves cutting a 1/4″ × 12″ slit in the face of any cabinet or bulkhead, behind which an accessible 6″ × 6″ × 12″ space exists. (Paper towel rolls are usually of 5″ diameter.) Simply dropping the roll in place and feeding it through the slot will not be sufficient. You will have to have a dowel axle system. A hole in the bottom of the cupboard will seat the dowel while a deeper hole in the top will let you slip it up and then down into place. If the space is not of appropriate size, a store-bought plastic holder will do nicely here.

THE FINELY FITTED YACHT

PAPER TOWEL RACK

THE PROPER PUMP

Well now. Let's roll up the shirt sleeves, clench the fists and start swinging, for I'm sure little will be accomplished by reasoning about pumps, for all of you have your favourite one that you cuddle and cherish. But when it snorts and burps and sputters and comes apart in your loving hands, you'll be happy you have read the following.

Very few of the mobile home conversion pumps, which many small boat manufacturers insist upon, have any long-lasting value. My niece's doll house has better built equipment. First of all, these pumps had a poor upbringing: they spit. The water from them does not flow, it comes in restless little ejaculations and even that, only after one nervously whips the delicate little handle back and forth a few dozen times. But heaven forbid thirst at sea, for the delicate little handle was designed to be used with perfect muscle and weight control, so the slightest lurch or shifting that places more than 18 ounces of pressure on the little jewel will result in its becoming a chromed pretzel.

Electrical pumps are cute and funny. You haven't really laughed until you've seen the owner of a $100,000 floating palace lying on his belly sucking water out of his tanks after the cute electric motor has given up the ghost.

Foot pumps are great as long as they're out of the way, like in a drawer or in the basement.

Now for the real pumps. Nothing in the world can replace the old-fashioned draw pump. Various designs have been used for hundreds of years, drawing jillions of gallons of water in their lifetimes. The Romans used it, the Arabs used it, the Italians still use it, so who are you to snub it? Most are built like cannons, heavy brass that's hard to bend and harder to break, and also hard to pump, but then two pumpings will fill the largest tea mug. The handles swivel 180° to accommodate right or left handers; they come beautifully chromed or irresistably polished with large solid knobs that fit snugly in your palms, and the insides are all brass, and they never need priming, and they never bend, never stick and never break, and ours have worked flawlessly for three years, one in the head and one in the galley and one in a little lighted niche for daily adoration.

THE PROPER PUMP

HINGED COUNTER

A very simple and fine solution for adding working surface to a galley without cutting permanently into any walking areas, is the addition of a small fold-down table to the end of a counter. Granted, it will not have the strength and usability of a fixed cabinet, but it will be a great help during food preparation when a place is needed to put a pot while a stove is lit or icebox lid opened.

The hinged counter in its simplest form can be a piece of 1/2″ plywood, painted, oiled or varnished, and trimmed with 1/2″ teak or mahogany. If the counter is to open into a fore-and-aft passageway, one would be wise to reach a compromise in design to allow a person to at least squeak by the open counter, if absolutely necessary. A counter I've seen that, in use, completely blocked a passageway was eventually ripped out by the owner because he got sick and tired of crawling under it. For support, the store-bought collapsible metal arms will do nicely (brass would look the best) unless one wants to save money and fabricate a hinged plywood knee (see seat for "Forepeak Desk Conversion"). In either case, the trim must be run about one inch past the bottom edge of the plywood to create a space for stowing the hinged support. I can see no need for fiddles on the counter top, for I very much doubt that anyone would undertake a meal at sea elaborate enough to require the additional counter space. The trim should be cut on 45° corners, glued, and screwed to the plywood with #8 P.H.S.M. screws and plugged. If desired, brass tacks can be substituted to save time. Round the corners of the trim generously. Affix a barrel bolt to the cabinet face, and drill a corresponding hole in the edge of the hinged counter to keep it from swinging when folded down. If nothing else, it will make a perfect little shelf for a vase.

HINGED COUNTER

POT HOLES

Why would anyone in his right mind want pot holes in his boat, you ask. The answer is simple: to keep pots in, of course. The source of this most ingenious idea is again Susan and Eric Hiscock, who have, aboard *Wanderer IV*, more pot holes than all of Tijuana's roads combined. They are very close to being the perfect solution to pot stowage — enabling removal of any single pot without disturbing others, eliminating the possibility of any rattling and clanging at sea, and being extremely simple to construct and adapt to any vessel's cabinetry. Beyond all that, they have one great advantage over any other pot stowage method I can think of, in that the lid to each pot can be stowed *in* the pot, again eliminating endless digging and searching through some bottomless pit. When at sea, the lids can be stowed upside down in the pots to lower their center of gravity and make less likely their escape.

Into most above-counter cabinets, at least two shelves of holes can be installed. The pots having the largest surfaces should be on the top shelf where the curvature of the hull usually allows more room.

Rough cut 1/2″ sheets of plywood to fit, then lay out all your pots and pans and arrange them in the most economical order. Don't forget to leave space for the handles in such a fashion that they will be readily accessible. Draw in the shape of each pot and cut out the hole with a jigsaw very accurately, remembering that any overcutting will result in irritating rattles under way. Very shallow pots, like frying pans, whose handles prevent them from slipping into a hole to sufficient depth will require the fabrication of chocks, the height of which will be determined by the lip. Three short ones will do. Install these to make a very snug fit. Round the edges of the holes with sandpaper to prevent splintering. Next, lay out the position of the shelves inside the cabinet and install either 3/4″ cleat stock or quarter-round as shelf supports. Glue and screw them into place. Sand all edges of the shelves, then screw the shelves onto the cleats. Do not use glue here, for you may one day get sick of your current pots or you may one day lose some of them overboard and logic tells me that it would be infinitely easier to make new holes for the new pots, than to hammer a pot to fit properly into the old holes.

POT HOLES

POT HOLDERS

Pots and pans in cupboards take up vast amounts of valuable space and make much noise. Every effort should be made to relocate them onto a bulkhead, where they can hang out of the way with the counterspace below them still fruitfully utilized. Of course, if your pots are ugly, forget this suggestion and store the damned things in the bilge.

Decorative copper-bottomed pots are not all that costly, and with a bit of regular polishing they look splendid on any yacht.

If your pots have no metal loops at the ends of the handles, you will have to drill an eighth-inch hole and fabricate a leather loop yourself.

Arrange your pots in order of size, and mark the end of the loop of each on the bulkhead. In aligning them, it is best to use a centreline through the middle of the pots. Lining up tops or bottoms tends to look less balanced.

At each mark on the bulkhead, drill a 1/4″ hole downward at 45°. Drill about 3/4″ deep, bulkhead permitting. Next, cut 1/4″ dowel stock into 1¾″ lengths. Round the fresh edges with sandpaper, then glue them into the holes. Try to have even lengths protruding.

From soft leather, cut one 1¼″ × 5½″ strip per pot. Trim the corners to a radius — it looks more civilized. Have a canvas shop insert grommets (or do it yourself if you have a grommet press) for twist-locks at one end of the strap. Install the straps on the bulkhead at the base of the handle with a single screw. Be sure to use a finish washer. It looks better, and it will keep the leather from ripping out. Attach the twist end of the twist-lock to the bulkhead in a position where firm tension will be placed on the straps. Your pots will remain silent in even the roughest seas.

Just keep those bottoms gleaming.

POT HOLDERS

KNIFE BLOCK

Those most circumspect will realize that I call this a knife *block*, and not a "rack". A knife rack, which somehow grips the handles and allows the sadistic little blades to whirl about at sea, has no place on a boat. The blades should be fully sheathed and securely pinched so they remain benign carving tools.

The simplest method of construction involves one piece of 2" × 6" or 2" × 4" (depending on how many knives you want to stow). The length of wood required is twice the length of the longest blade, plus an inch.

Thus, step one is to buy the knives. No way on earth can you hope to make a perfectly fitting block for an imaginary set. Blade length and thickness will determine all measurements.

Try to buy a set that will: a) last, and b) be easily replaceable in case a member of the first set decides to dive into the sea. Nothing is more difficult to remodel than a knife block. Except maybe a needle.

Without cutting the piece of board into two halves, secure the thinnest table saw blade possible, and cut the slits for each knife with the saw blade set at *half* the depth of the widest part of the specific knife blade. Be sure to cut the groove to the exact depth, otherwise the blades will wander about in a rolling or pitching boat and irritatingly dull themselves.

Once grooved, cut the board into two equal pieces and mate them, like closing a book. Your grooves will be perfectly aligned. Now, drill four holes between the grooves (from the back so that the holes won't show), and glue and screw the halves together. Bullnose the edges of the front and top. Next, drill two mounting screw holes from the front, and countersink them judiciously. If you're setting the block on a countertop, place a bead of silicone around the perimeter of the bottom to prevent a stagnant pool of water from forming beneath.

The location is obvious. Leave enough room above to allow removal of the longest knife. A narrow part of the counter that's unusable as a working surface would be an ideal spot. The block is more suited to sit on something anyway, so its bulk will be reduced visually.

Try to mount it athwartships. If mounted fore and aft, the rolling of the boat may cause the heavy handles to pendulum with the blades hacking the block on every roll. Galley knives are not for wood chopping.

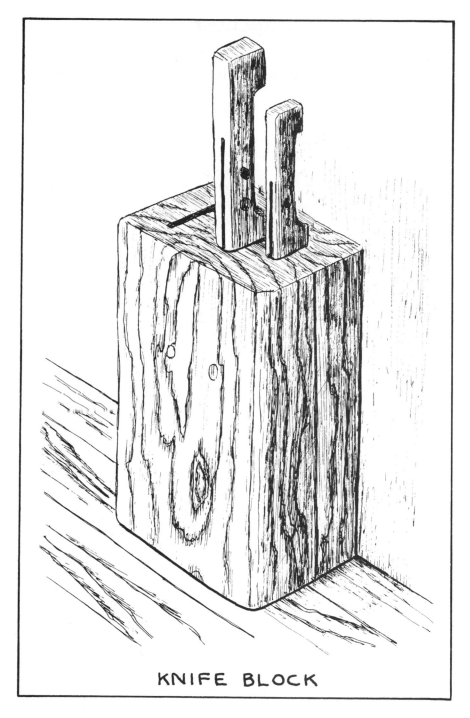

KNIFE BLOCK

TOASTER

Having gone through a number of store-bought, stove top toasters made of landlubber tin that rusts at the first whiff of salt air, and little stainless steel ones that toast one pathetic side of two flimsy pieces of bread at one time, I've been forced to design one of my own.

This one can be made of either stainless or brass sheeting of a fairly light gauge, and brass or copper wire of about 8 or 10 gauge.

It will very nicely toast one side of five pieces of bread at one time to a fine, even hue.

First, cut the sheeting to the shape shown, making the width of the base roughly the same as the diameter of your burner. Then draw concentric circles, spaced about 3/4″ apart, onto each half of the base plate. *But* stagger the radiuses from one plate to another, i.e. if the largest radius on your bottom plate is say 2 5/8″, then make the largest radius of your top plate 2¼″ (a reduction of one-half of the 3/4″ spacing). This is done to get the heat to circulate a bit between the two plates so that it will be fairly even by the time it reaches the toast. Now drill 1/16″ holes every half inch along each circle. Stagger these as well from bottom plate to top plate. Drill your screw holes as well for assembling the base, then bend the plates along the dotted line to 90°, but leave closing the jaws (bringing the two plates together) until later when you've bent the support wires into place. Actually, you should do that right now. Bend four pieces of the wire to the dimensions in the diagram, then slip them into the drilled holes and bend the last 3/4″ under sharply, as shown. Now pull them all together tightly, and join them in the upper corners with short bits of wire.

Lastly, pull the jaws together and secure them with #8 P.H.S.M. screws through the six screw holes indicated.

Not only will this unit toast your bread very efficiently, but after a few hours of heat, the metal will turn all sorts of beautiful colours.

Oh yes, the fifth piece of toast is laid over the tops of the four standing ones like a house of cards.

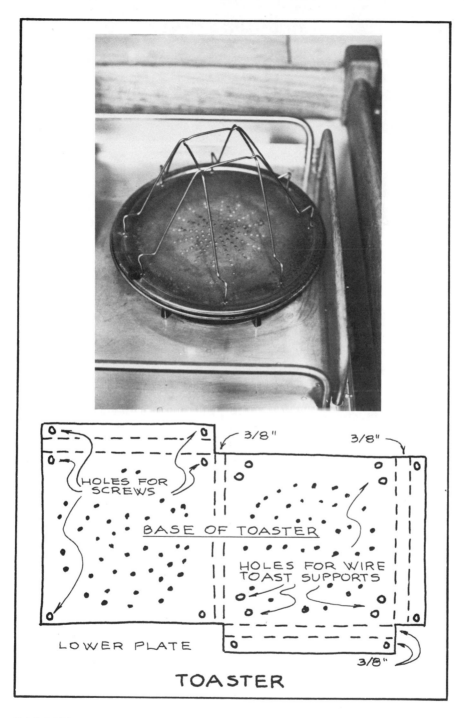

3/8"

3/8"

HOLES FOR
SCREWS

BASE OF TOASTER

HOLES FOR WIRE
TOAST SUPPORTS

LOWER PLATE

3/8"

TOASTER

SINGLE BURNER PRIMUS

In cooler northern climates, most yachts are equipped with a diesel cooking stove that also doubles as the ship's furnace. These units produce enough heat to keep the yacht cozy on the coldest of days, but their heat is too general and excessive for making a quick dinner or boiling water for tea on a warm summer day without overheating the entire cabin.

A good solution, although it may seem somewhat redundant financially and spacially, is to install a single burner, double-gimballed, kerosene stove (see illustration). The most reliable one is an all brass one made by Optimus which uses the same heavy duty burners that fire the best large kerosene stoves. The stove itself is mounted in the classic heavy cast aluminum bracket which mounts with four screws onto any bulkhead. The most beautiful aspect of the whole unit is that a single set-screw near the bracket's base quickly releases the entire apparatus, so if its mounting can be accomplished only in a somewhat inconvenient area, it can be kept stowed on most occasions and pulled out and inserted in place on very short notice. While storing, care must be taken not to turn the control knob to "ON", or the stove will leak kerosene everywhere. It should be stored in the most vertical position possible. The major drawback of the kerosene system is that the burner must be preheated with either alcohol or other priming fuels. This results in spillage on some occasions, so effort should be made to mount the stove over as resilient a surface as possible. The galley sink is best, your favourite bunk is worst.

The entire unit sells for under a hundred dollars, and judging by the testimony of yachtsmen who have suffered through summers with the heat-blasting diesel stove, the investment pays wonderful dividends.

A word of caution that's worth repeating everytime one discusses kerosene burners — the tiny hole, where the vaporized kerosene is released to the burner, is closed off and cleaned with a very delicate built-in needle. If the control knob is turned too violently to the "CLEAN" position, the fragile needle is liable to break off and render the burner useless. Because replacement parts are so difficult to find, you'll probably have to replace the entire burner at the rather formidable price of $30. So use tact. This is a fine mechanism, not a wrist exerciser.

SINGLE BURNER PRIMUS

STOVE UNDER CHOPPING BOARD

On all small cruising vessels galley space is extremely precious. With the inclusion of the bare necessities such as a sink and stove, extremely little free counter surface remains for food preparation. A most useful area above the burners of cooking stoves that can, on almost any vessel, yield a 24″ × 16″ chopping board *cum* work surface, remains to be exploited. I found the most thoughtful of these retractable boards on the Dutch ketch *"Areité."*

The board consisted of two long pieces hinged in the middle, that, in turn, hinge up together, out of the way, behind the stove (see diagram). The stock used should be 13/16″, preferably two solid pieces whose combined widths equal the depth of the stove. If you already have a chopping board and need only counterspace, the solid wood will still be less expensive in the long run than plywood with formica over, because of the vulnerability of formica to heat which may cause it to bubble. The ideal wood for a chopping board is maple, but any other, like oak, would suffice. Avoid teak, for it tends to flavour foods.

Cut your stock to fit over the stove allowing 1/4″ clearance at each end between board and cabinetry. Next, cut two lengths of cleat stock to run along the cabinets and act as supports for the board. Bullnose the free edge for a nice effect, then glue, screw, and plug. Round the edges of the boards slightly with sandpaper.

Acquire some very thin copper or stainless steel sheeting (so thin you can bend it with finger tip effort) in a quantity sufficient to cover one side and all edges of each board. I think this is mandatory for even though the board will be held away from the stove with barrel bolts when flames are present, the possibility of a "slip" still exists which would let the boards fall over the exposed flames. The sheet metal will give considerable protection in such an event. So, cut the metal, lay the board over it, then cut in at the corners and fold the metal onto the edges and tack every three inches with small brass tacks. Now, using four 2″ hinges join the boards together on the undersides and, in turn, join the board to the cabinetry behind the stove so the boards will fold up and stow in this vertical position (see diagram). Affix a single barrel bolt to the top inboard corner of the inboard board and drill two holes in the adjoining counter to hold the boards in either their open or closed position. Oil lightly with mineral oil.

THE FINELY FITTED YACHT

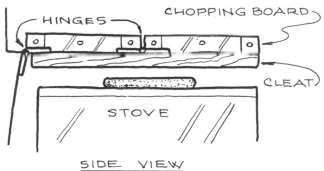

HINGES   CHOPPING BOARD

CLEAT

STOVE

SIDE VIEW

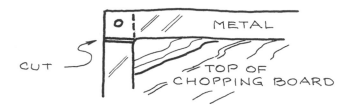

METAL

CUT

TOP OF CHOPPING BOARD

CHOPPING BOARD OVER STOVE

STOVE GUARDRAIL

If your galley is U-shaped with your stove aligned fore and aft (I defy you to gimball a stove mounted athwartships), a stove guardrail must be installed. Contrary to its name, the rail guards not the stove but the cook, from a flaming belly flop. As well as being a fence, which prevents inadvertent twisting of knobs by careless hips and derrières resulting in overruns of kerosene or alcohol, it is also a terrific place to hang dish towels. In short: build it!

Purchase two sets of stainless steel or brass dinghy gudgeons and pintles, and install the gudgeons on the cabinet sides so the rail when installed in the pintles will line up with the counter searails. Be certain to allow sufficient space between rail and stove so that the latter can swing freely. This setup will let you remove the rail at will without causing any damage.

A single piece of 13/16″ teak about 3″ wide will be all the wood needed. This should be cut to a length that will fit snugly into the pintles while in the gudgeons. Radius the corners, bullnose all around, and bolt on the pintles.

To keep the cook from falling *away* from the stove, a padeye should be installed at each end of the rail. These must be through-bolted. If masterfully planned or craftily re-bent, the holes in the padeyes and the pintles will be aligned allowing the use of a single bolt. Use cap nuts. No chef likes to get his wrists scratched before having them slapped.

A length of seat belt (measurement depending on the obesity of the most frequent cook) should have a snap shackle sewn onto either end. It can be clipped quickly into place in heavy seas. Do not make the belt too tight — give the cook room to turn and twist. Just provide a secure brace so his hands will remain free to stir the browning sugar for the Crème Caramel.

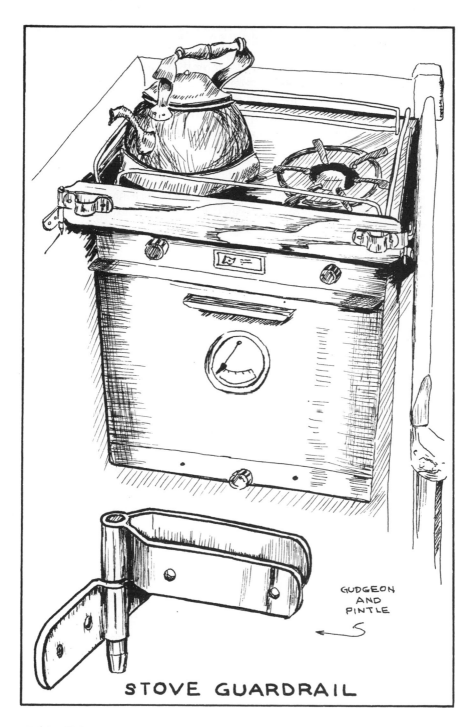

GUDGEON
AND
PINTLE

STOVE GUARDRAIL

THE GALLEY SEAT

We hunted down this beautifully crafted piece on *Scorpion*, a sleek 46' Argentinian ketch, cruising in Antiguan waters during Antigua's Sailing Week, which is an absolute must see for anyone who likes pageantry, gallant yachts, and wonderful people from as far away as Norway and New Zealand. Where was I? If you don't have a U-shaped galley, accept my profound sorrow, and begin building your galley seat.

Brass or stainless tubing of 1½" or 2" diameter makes an ideal main support. You need about a 5' length. If you have access to a plumbing or machine shop that can put a 90° bend into the pipe, have it bent making the vertical leg 26" and the horizontal piece as short as possible. As obvious from the illustration, this sort of an arrangement is not the easiest to anchor, so the shorter you can make the horizontal lever arm, the fewer problems you'll have with heavy leaning bodies. Under no circumstances should you have the two pieces cut at 45° angles and then welded. The vicious point you'd be creating would be massacring thighs daily. Have a 4" diameter base plate welded to each end with two triangulated supports to reinforce the welds. While at the welders, have him attach a small plate where you will be putting the wooden seat pad.

Drill 1/4" holes in your base plates and, using a single backup plate instead of large washers, bolt the base plates to the cabinet and cabin sole. Now, fabricate a seat from 1¾" × 4" × 6" teak. Anything larger would be a waste. This is not a throne. It's a place for the cook to rest momentarily before he returns to the bubbling cauldron. Whatever shape your seat, round the corners and bullnose the edges. Attach it to the bracket with #10 sheet metal screws. Now, invite down your *mom-in-lawus gargantuanus* to test it.

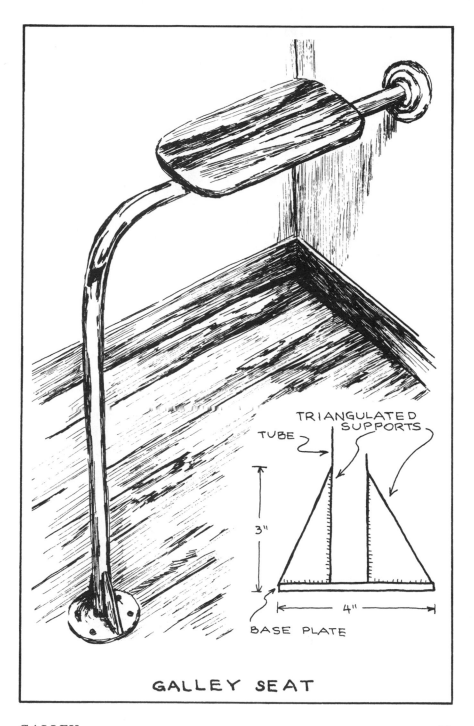

TRIANGULATED
SUPPORTS

TUBE

3"

BASE PLATE

4"

GALLEY SEAT

CHOPPING BOARD

Construction of a comely chopping board can be a rewarding investment of one's time. There are no real finicky touches, no delicate measurements, and the results are, in most cases, delightful.

The hardwoods best suited are the non-oily ones like maple or oak, although people have mixed many woods with different tones and grains for effect. The only types to be avoided are woods like teak which have so much oil that they tend to transfer some of it along with a definite unpleasant flavour to foods left on them for any length of time.

Longevity can best be guaranteed by using end grain for the chopping surface. If the grain of the wood is laid along the surface, grooving and slivering will quickly occur and total board death will not be far behind.

The board should not be extravagantly large. Hardwoods are very heavy and no sea cook need be burdened with the task of controlling a behemoth at sea. If such a thing as general size can be given, then the figure of 100 square inches is probably a good one. Thickness should be 1½″. The board will be of a manageable weight and size and can double as a cheese and bread board, obviating the use of a number of plates.

The actual measurements should be guided by possible stowage locations. Since it is a weighty object, it can gain momentum at sea unless carefully corralled. We have an 11″ counter space in a corner of our galley framed athwartships by cabinet face and the searail, thus, measurements of our board became 11″ X 9″. Stowed here when not in use, it has become an ideal base for hot pots and pans which would otherwise damage the varnished countertops.

Ideally, wide boards should be acquired to minimize the work involved; since you only need about one lineal foot of a 2″ X 8″ board, acquisition should be no problem. Any woodworking shop would be happy to sell you an end piece that size if you can't find it in a lumber yard. Be certain that the board is not warped or your task will be impossible. Sand and fair both sides of the board, then cut it into 1½″ strips and glue and bar clamp. Use waterproof plastic resin or resorcinol glue only. Remember to assemble end grain up. Try to have the surface of each strip flush with the others for end grain is very difficult to plane and almost as difficult to sand. Allow it to set overnight, then remove the clamps and detail. Oil with a couple of coats of flavourless mineral oil.

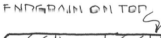

ENDGRAIN ON TOP

1/4" ALL-THREAD TO KEEP BOARD
FROM DELAMINATING UNDER
CONSTANT EXPANSION/CONTRACTION
OF BEING SOAKED, THEN DRYING OUT.

CHOPPING BOARD

THE DISH RACK

If you think, for a moment, that the teak dish rack in the illustration is a complicated thing to fabricate, then you're absolutely right. But so what, a good mind thrives on challenge.

The very first step is to determine location. The rack drawn is in *Warm Rain*, directly over the ice box, which is built athwartships between the galley and the salon. With its very open design, the rack allows a flow of air and light and conversation through the ship, yet it does serve as a bit of a visual divider, making the salon a secluded area. As a further division, Candace usually slings a net of fresh fruit below the rack from one end to the other. The openness of the rack has another most practical aspect in that the dishes can be reached from the salon without one's having to actually leave the table.

The entire rack can be made to hang from the overhead without the benefit of support from the inboard pole you see in the illustration, however, a little reinforcement can go a long way, especially when it can double as a handhold as well.

The construction of the dish rack is similar to a drawer with partitions. Its bottom is of 1/2″ plywood, the rest is 13/16″ teak.

The size of the rack should be dictated by two factors: 1) the amount of space available, and 2) the amount and size of dishes you regard as indispensable to preserve the style to which you are accustomed. This latter point is no laughing matter. To function perfectly and look its possible best, the dish rack will have to be designed for a certain set of dishes, so choose most thoughtfully and thoroughly.

And here a few words on dishes may be meritorious. Yacht dishes are like no others in the functions they are called upon to perform in the most absurd of conditions. Peas and soups are required to stay inside them on the most absurd angles, gravy is not to be spilled from them even if they're going back and forth like a teeter-totter, and they're morally bound to keep various foods warm while the crew saunters off for a sail change or a look-see. Thus, four points can be deemed to be of top priority when the selection is being made: depth, stability, height of rim, and insulative ability.

Depth

This is most important in mugs and soup bowls. A deep dish, half filled, will have a much lesser chance of spilling when tilted than a necessarily fuller shallow one. This is vital when food is being carried, or being eaten from the lap.

DISH RACK

Stability

This is of utmost consideration. Most plates or bowls with sloping sides and wide rims need only to be tapped anywhere along the perimeter and they'll willingly spill half their contents before they stabilize themselves again. A totally flat-bottomed dish, on the other hand, would take a fat lady from the circus standing on its rim before it would behave in an unhousebroken manner (see diagram).

Height of Rim

A landlubber rimless plate has no place on a yacht. Even an experienced tightrope walker would have difficulty keeping his food corralled, and I speak not only of stormy sea conditions, but of any time a runabout passes by or someone steps off the side deck. Plates with vertical lips of as little as $1/2''$ will very nicely hold gravy, salad dressing, rolling peas, toast and even sliding ice cream, safely in place.

Insulative Ability

A heavy ceramic plate or mug, if preheated, will keep food and drinks warm for a long time. Light ceramic or plastic dinnerware has the insulative characteristics of a Kleenex.

With these four factors in mind, we searched store after store for the proper dinnerware and after much frustration, ended up having a dear friend make us a heavy earthenware set to our own specifications. The bottoms of all dishes are completely flat, as Plate B in the diagram. The plates have lips, the soup bowls are deep, and the mugs are large and heavy enough to be used as weapons. With the weight, their one disadvantage is that if dropped they leave dents in the woodwork, but we've been taking anti-oaf lessons and getting much better.

So pick your dishes, then decide the approximate surface area for each shelf and lay it out on a piece of paper. Your mugs should be no problem, just arrange a shelf wide enough to house them. The handles can hang out of slots as shown. Take your plates and bowls and arrange and rearrange them until a balanced and accessible pattern has been found, containing as little wasted space as possible. Don't forget to allow $13/16''$ between the dishes for the divider baffles.

Next, establish how the outboard end of the rack is to be secured. We worked ours into the grab/drip rail of the edge of the underdeck. If you own no such rail, just run about $3''$ of the shelf under the side decks and fasten it to same with glue/mishmash and screws. The inboard end, as mentioned, is best supported by a pole,

a. REGULAR PLATE

PRESSURE ON
POINTS INDICATED
BY ARROWS
WOULD FLIP "a"
BUT NOT "b"

b. FLAT-BOTTOMED PLATE

DIAGRAM A - DISH STABILITY

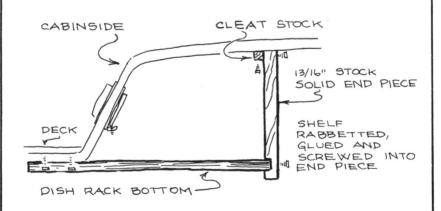

CABINSIDE

CLEAT STOCK

13/16" STOCK
SOLID END PIECE

SHELF
RABBETTED,
GLUED AND
SCREWED INTO
END PIECE

DECK

DISH RACK BOTTOM

DIAGRAM B - RACK SUPPORTS

DISH RACK

but if that's not possible, a solid end piece can be attached to the shelf and secured to the overhead with cleat stock (see diagram). To assist somewhat, the sides of the rack will be rabbetted to let in the shelf then, with the means of cleat stock, secured to the cabin side.

If you are going to use a post, then, from 1½″ stock, cut a square post and bullnose all edges with 3/8″ bullnose. Now, cut away half of the post stock on its first 6″ to make room for the ice box, or whatever the lower end is to be fastened to. Next, from the point where the bottom of the low side of the rack is to intercept the post, dado the post as in Diagram C. You'll have to clean out the last couple of inches with a chisel.

For the sides of the rack, try to determine a good average height, one that will safely keep your plates, but not one that looks absurdly weighty. Remember, it's aesthetically much more pleasant if all the sides and baffles are of the same height, instead of jutting up here and poking out there like some sort of unsolved Chinese puzzle. Mark the centre of each compartment onto the low side pieces.

You will be butting up all baffles to sides, so just cut them to length and assemble them dry and keep checking the fit from time to time with the dishes. When everything is cut and fitted, pencil in all your baffles onto the shelf and drill pilot holes every six or so inches, brush a bit of glue onto each baffle, put them back into place one by one and, using the pilot holes as guides, countersink from the *bottom* of the plywood shelf, and fasten the baffles to the shelf with #10 P.H.S.M.'s. Where you have access, put a screw through the side of one baffle into the endgrain of another. At other places, just brush glue onto the endgrain and stick in place, and let the bottom screws do the work.

The small dead spaces can be left open for storage of odds and ends, or if they are too narrow to be of any use, just fashion a small lid out of 1/4″ teak and glue it over the crevasse, otherwise, it'll just become a filthy, fallow hole.

Round all edges smartly and oil.

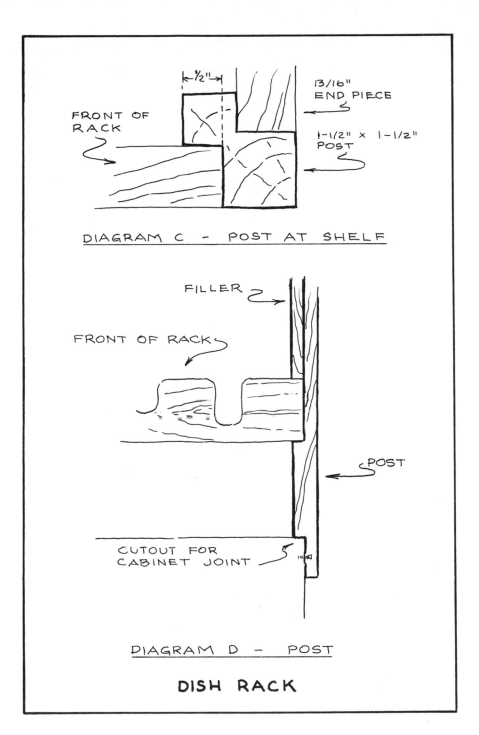

½"

13/16"
END PIECE

FRONT OF
RACK

1-1/2" x 1-1/2"
POST

DIAGRAM C - POST AT SHELF

FILLER

FRONT OF RACK

POST

CUTOUT FOR
CABINET JOINT

DIAGRAM D - POST

DISH RACK

THROUGH-BULKHEAD ACCESS

Now we're getting down to the bizarre details that make a yacht such a place of wonder. In numerous instances, small access holes through bulkheads would be most advantageous to flip a switch, or turn a valve, or just to have a quick glance into the engine room to verify that all is as should be. This quick removal hatch can obviate the need for unhinging steps and doors and drops.

I shall concentrate on the engine room bulkhead for: a) that is the one most frequently needing this little critter, and b) the critter for this bulkhead is the most complex to make because it is usually sound insulated.

Since we are normally concerned with a finished bulkhead of either oiled or painted wood, the utmost care must be taken when work is being done so as not to damage any surfaces. First, ascertain the location of your access hatch, remembering that wrists and fingers bend but forearms don't. Next, with a 1/4" drill bit, drill a hole through the center of the assigned area. A 4" hole saw will be needed for the hatch itself. (Four inches seems to be large enough for the mightiest fist.) With the bit set long to act as a guide, carefully cut the hole. Hold the drill motor steady or you'll make a hell of a mess of the bulkhead. Once cut, remove the piece from your hole saw and, for heaven's sake, don't throw it away, for this will comprise the hatch itself. Sand the edges of the hole and hatch to avoid chipping, and plug the 1/4" hole with a wood plug. Chisel off and finish. Attach a small brass padeye to the center of the hatch for a handle. Cut a thick strip of leather, and stretch, glue, and tack it around the circumference of the hatch. This will act to hold the hatch snug when in place, and seal off any engine noise. The hatch is now ready to use, working much like a cork in a bottle. Attempting to hinge it would prove unsuccessful, both functionally and aesthetically for: a) a snug fit would not be possible and through the crack would come engine noise and engine smell, and b) a hinge, no matter how small, would look sort of silly, and would most likely necessitate the use of a latch as well.

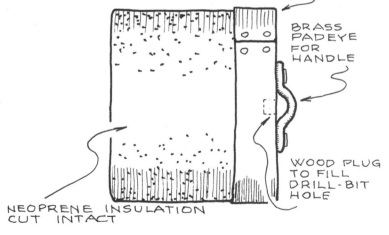

BULKHEAD PIECE WITH LEATHER WRAPPING FOR TIGHT FIT

BRASS PADEYE FOR HANDLE

WOOD PLUG TO FILL DRILL-BIT HOLE

NEOPRENE INSULATION CUT INTACT

BULKHEAD CUTOUT DOOR

THROUGH-BULKHEAD ACCESS

LA BOÎTE DE GARBAGE

Everything has been tried: plastic bags, paper bags, buckets, and old boots, yet none has proved to be an ideal garbage container for a yacht. Unsupported plastic bags collapse, paper bags leak, buckets roll about, and boots smell. A container, firmly affixed, easily accessible, and quickly removable, must be fabricated. Two major varieties exist: the slip-in top-loading, removable top type, as found on Bristol Channel Cutters and CT 38's, or the fixed-onto-hinged-door types, as found on Ontario 32's. These are both extremely functional, the former, because it can be located on top of a galley counter and things can be swept rapidly into it, the latter, because it can be fabricated with much ease.

Top-Loading

The basic structure of the top-loader is a box built of 3/8" plywood and thoroughly painted. If you can find a top-loading galley locker that is not now used to its fullest advantage (ho-ho-ho), then you are halfway there. Line the rim of the opening with milled or laminated seating cleats. Since drilling and screwing will be well nigh impossible from within, unless you are a retired India rubber man, just glue and clamp the cleats in place.

Fabricate your plywood box to slip past the cleats, and line its top with a holding cleat of 3/8" plywood, protruding 1/4" all the way around. This should be glued and screwed in place, or, if preferred for added strength, a 5/8" cleat stock can be run around the inside perimeter; the holding cleat may then be secured to this. The latter is a more positive configuration, providing a little hand hold, as well, for removal. Paint the inside of the box thoroughly with a couple of coats of good gloss paint, and line it with throwaway plastic bags.

Hinged-Door Type

Find a front loading locker whose inboard end is scarcely used, and find a plastic waste paper pail that will fit nicely onto it, and screw it to the door. And you had to buy a book to find this out. Oh well!

THE FINELY FITTED YACHT

LA BOÎTE

DROP DOOR GARBAGE STOWAGE

A drop door equipped with a small plywood bin seems to be a perfectly ideal garbage container. The box should be formed as shown and, if made as large as possible, it will more or less accommodate the plastic garbage bags that usually measure 20″ X 20″.

On one side of the box, a shallow sleeve will hold the spare plastic bags, while an even smaller sleeve will be made to accommodate the wire or plastic twisties that seal the bags.

The depth of the box need be no more than 6″ at the bottom, flaring to about 12″ at the top. The angle of the top of the box is critical; it should slope away from the door in such a fashion that measurement X on the diagram will be about 1/2″ less than the height of the door opening.

To construct, cut 3/8″ plywood to form the bottom and three sides, assemble using cleat stock, glue, and screw. Cut a small slit about 1″ deep and 1/8″ wide into the tops of the sides of the bin where it meets the door. This is to accommodate the edge of the plastic bag which can be slipped down into the slit to keep the bag from collapsing. The sleeve for spare bags and twisties can be made from a single piece of 1/8″ plywood, set on a frame of 3/4″ cleat stock. The size of the sleeves should total about 7″ X 7″, with the twistie taking up about 1″ of one side. Paint the interior of the bin generously to seal off any cracks; you do not want leaky garbage leaking all over your lockers.

To minimize the odours drifting out and about the yacht, cut a simple lid from 3/8″ plywood and hinge it from the door. Line the edges of the lid with weatherstripping (self-adhesive foam strips are available in rolls at hardware stores) for a perfect seal. If you're fussy, install a hook and eye to keep the lid closed securely. Paint or varnish the lid to keep it from warping or staining.

Lastly, attach a length of brass chain a few inches from the bin, both to the door and the cabinet, to keep the door from flying wide open and dumping the garbage on the cabin sole. Make the end of the door a permanent attachment, but make the cabinet end detachable (just slip the last link of the chain over a cup hook), so the door can be lowered into a fully open position, should access to the locker's bowels be required.

DROP DOOR GARBAGE STOWAGE

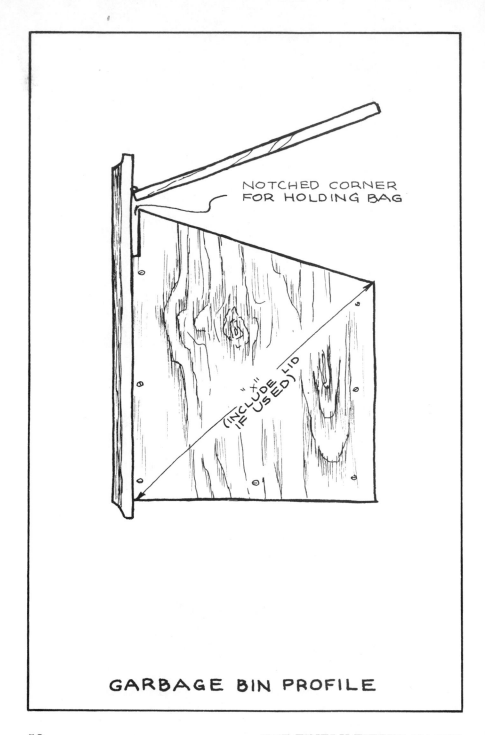

NOTCHED CORNER
FOR HOLDING BAG

("INCLUDE "X"
IF USED) LID

GARBAGE BIN PROFILE

SOAP DISPENSER

More often than not I'm against anything that's unnecessarily mechanized, believing strongly in simple things that have no breakable parts like a plastic bottle of liquid soap. Yet now, there exists such a beautifully designed and carefully crafted dispenser that I must mention and even recommend it for all galleys, and perhaps heads.

As shown in the photo, the visible chrome part is only 2½" tall, and the entire thing requires less than 2" of horizontal space on a counter, spout included. It is visually appealing and quite nicely eliminates the unsightly Joy bottle which, after a few days, collects dirty fingerprints, and with its label half soaked and smeared, creates a disgusting sight even among dirty dishes, and that's bad.

The dispenser requires one hole in the counter top for installation. Choose your location well, keeping in mind that the spout should overhang the sink, but that sufficient space must be left beneath to unscrew the refillable bottle, which itself is 7" × 2". As mentioned, it could be put to good use in the head as well, if you don't mind smelling a little like a department store washroom. One of the more splendid locations for one of these critters would be, I feel, in a cutout near the cockpit where fish cleaning and clothes washing as well as hand and dishwashing often occur. It can be totally out of the way in a niche and refilled simply from below; and best of all, no one need ever worry about slipping on a bar of soap.

head

TEAK FOLDING SINK

Back when fine work was a point of pride with most craftsmen, beautiful things, such as this sink, were a common sight. It consists of solid teak or mahogany, and some profound stainless steel work. If you are satisfied with a 10″ diameter sink, the entire cabinet need be no more than 24″ × 18″ × 4″.

Begin by building the frame of the cabinet (the part to be fastened to bulkhead). Rip 13/16″ stock to 3¼″ width, and butt them and screw them, or dovetail them, with a jig (see "Tools"), and glue them to make up the 18″ × 24″ frame. Next, cut the fixed face piece to a 6″ width and screw it temporarily to the lower part of the frame. Drill a 1″ diameter hole in the centre of the bottom of your frame for a drainpipe. Now, from a 5′ piece of 6″ wide board of 13/16″. teak, cut the trapezoid shaped pieces for your sink base as shown in Diagram A. Join them together as in the illustration with the help of a doweling jig (see "Tools"). Next, mill from similar stock 1½″ pieces to make up an on-edge frame of 16″ × 18″ o.d.

When the glue has dried on your assembled trapezoids, draw a 10″ diameter circle in their centre and cut it out with a jigsaw to make room for the sink. Now, screw and glue the 16″ × 18″ frame to the trapezoids leaving a 1″ perimeter around the sides and top, which will force a 2″ part of the frame past the bottom of the trapezoids. This will make up the drain lip once the stainless steel is in place. Since the whole cabinet is to be lined with stainless, you will have to allow a little room for it when the drip lip becomes vertical. This can be accomplished by rabbetting the overhanging two inches of the frame by running it through the table saw for two cuts. See Diagram B. Now, take all the pieces and the illustrations down to your favourite sheet metal man and watch him die of laughter. When he resurrects, discuss what you need, explaining carefully that the lower portion of the cabinet, behind the temporarily attached 6″ piece, is to be a watertight well into which water will pour when the sink is tipped. With that in mind have him: a) weld a 3/4″ drain pipe to its bottom, b) hammer a lip around the edge of the frame to keep stray water in, and c) leave a 1/2″ wide lip bent to a 45° angle hanging *past* the 2″ drip lip frame. Now, tell him you don't want any rude talk, you just want your sink hammered out and adjoining parts made and installed a.s.a.p., and walk out. When you've restocked your savings account, leave on a hunt for a beautiful brass pump that mounts on the bulkhead, and fits snugly into a 10″ diameter sink.

Bon voyage.

FOLDED UP

TEAK FOLDING SINK

MEDICINE CABINET

Although I don't care a great deal for this idea, I do think that since you have to have a mirror in the head anyway, you may as well put a box behind it. It should *not*, of course, be used to contain the equipment of the first-aid kid. That should be put in a transportable container, like a good fishing tackle box, so the whole thing can be taken quickly to the injury, instead of dragging the injury down below and getting yuk all over the cushions.

Now, design the size of your cabinet to fit unobtrusively into the head, being certain that the mirror won't shatter against the bronze portlight on first opening of the cabinet door. General size need be no more than 12" × 15", but most importantly, it should be no deeper overall (door included) than 3½". This leaves a useable shelf depth of 2¼", which will accommodate most things yet will prevent the stacking of things behind each other.

Rip the four sides from 13/16" stock to 2¾" width. Rip your 1/4" thick shelves to the same width, less 1/8" to allow for the plywood back. Allow enough length so that 1/4" of the shelf can be let into the sides. Leave a space of about 6" between two shelves, and 4" between the others. Next, set your table saw at 1/8" height and, leaving 1/8" between the blade and the guard rail, run each shelf and the two vertical sides through once. This slight groove will accommodate searails of 1/8" plexiglass which: a) takes up little space, and b) allow you to see what's behind them. Next, rabbet the back of the sides to 1/8" depth to let in the plywood back. Glue everything well, and tack and glue the back onto the shelves as well as the frames. Measure for the door. Cut your frame pieces from 13/16" stock. Put a double rabbet into each frame to accommodate a 1/8" thick mirror backed by 1/8" plywood. See diagram. Lap joint your frame, glue and clamp, and allow it to set overnight. Drop in the mirror and the plywood and hold it in place with tacks running parallel to the plywood.

Next, cut 1½" strips from 1/8" plexiglass, remembering to add the 1/4" in length to allow for the grooves in the cabinet sides. Sand the edges, and pop each strip into place by bending it gently, then slipping it right down into the groove of the shelves.

Four sheet metal pan heads (with large washers beneath them) through the cabinet back should be sufficient mounting *if* you've glued and tacked the back on well. If not, good luck.

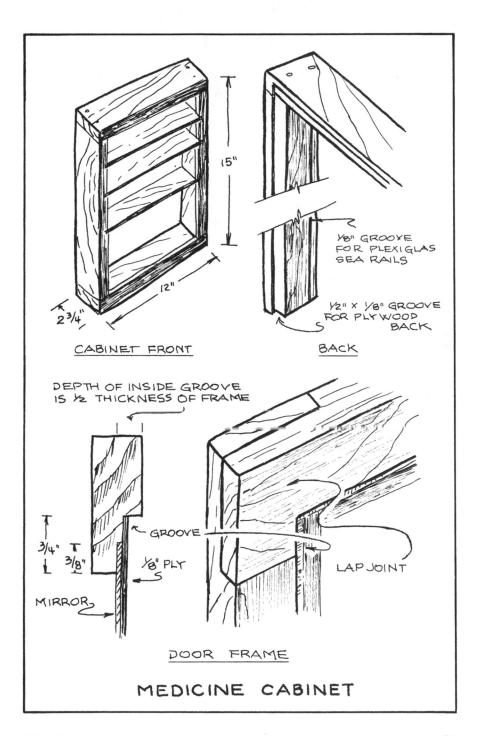

15"

12"

2¾"

CABINET FRONT

⅛" GROOVE
FOR PLEXIGLAS
SEA RAILS

½" x ⅛" GROOVE
FOR PLYWOOD
BACK

BACK

DEPTH OF INSIDE GROOVE
IS ½ THICKNESS OF FRAME

¾"

⅜"

GROOVE

⅛" PLY

MIRROR

LAP JOINT

DOOR FRAME

MEDICINE CABINET

TOOTHBRUSH AND CUP HOLDER

As shown in the photos, beautiful ready-made ware is available in brass and porcelain, neither inexpensive, and both very functional. The porcelain is Italian, and it's in *Warm Rain* mostly because we thought it would be easier to keep clean than brass.

Fabrication of toothbrush and soap dishes out of wood is promoted by many, but to me seems to be the height of folly, for both soap and toothpaste have a habit of soaking deep into teak and leaving unsightly stains. If home fabrication is to be attempted, the only logical material seems to be plexiglass.

For the toothbrush and cup holder, cut on a band saw from 1/2″ plexiglass stock, a 3½″ square piece, radiusing all corners, and lightly sanding all edges with 100 grit to make them less sharp. Cover the surfaces of the plexiglass with masking tape during all fabrication, to avoid scratches. Insert the piece face-up in a vise, using wooden padding to keep the plexiglass from getting marked, locate the centre point, and very carefully drill a 1/8″ pilot hole. Measure the diameter of the cup you will be using, at a point two-thirds up from the bottom. Remember not to use a perfectly cylindrical glass, for obvious reasons. Next, get a hole saw of that size, and drill through as vertically as possible. Now, in the four corners where the most available space exists, scratch in with a nail the shape of the stems of your favourite tooth brushes, then find a drill bit whose diameter is equal to the narrowest part of your pattern, and drill it through the centre. You will now have to gently play the drill bit back and forth until the entire area inside your nail line has been removed. Have only half the length of your drill bit in the hole, and try to avoid excessive up and down movements, lest you go down too far and the chuck of the drill gouges the plexiglass.

Now, sand all edges, then, from 1/4″ plexiglass stock, cut a piece 1½″ × 2″, radius the corners, and drill four 1/8″ holes in its corners, 3/8″ in from the sides. Using a square and an awl, lightly scratch a line parallel to the long sides, 1/2″ from the bottom. Using this line as a guide, cement the plate to the back of the holder with methylene chloride solvent, aligning the line with the bottom of the holder. Mount with round heads through the 1/8″ holes, and brush away.

TOOTHBRUSH HOLDER

HIDE-A-SINK

In any small head where the head itself faces athwartships a sliding hideaway sink can be installed to save space. To use, the sink slides out over the head and to stow, it slides outboard to the hull just below the side decks. The backrest attached to the inboard edge of the sink serves to hide the hole in the fore-and-aft bulkhead, which is necessary to allow the sink and related plumbing to slide "through."

The choice of sink will be determined by the amount of space available behind the head. When choosing, do not forget to allow for some sort of pump or faucet. Because this is a sliding platform, one would be unwise to equip it with a behemoth hand pump that might put unnecessary strain on the supports.

Cut the platform to fit from 3/4″ plywood, allowing space for 13/16″ trim on each end, plus 1/8″ for clearance. Thus the platform length = space - 1 7/8″

From 13/16″ stock, cut two 1½″ high rails to act as slides below the platform. Install them on the two athwartship bulkheads. Cover your platform with formica, etc., then cut it, and install the sink and pump. Now trim out the platform with similar pieces fore and aft and inboard, and a 4″ wide piece outboard. Arrange it so that half of this piece will stick up above the platform and half below. The "above" part will hide hoses and other apparatus while the "below" part will act as a stop to keep the platform from sliding out of its track. With this in mind, notch the ends of the stop to make space for the rails.

Next, attach the drain and intake hoses to the sink for a dry run just to determine how much of the fore-and-aft bulkhead will have to be cut away. Cut it and trim it out. With the trimmed out platform in "stow" position, lay the two top rails (to hold the platform down) into place, leaving 1/8″ clearance between it and the platform, and mark the back-stop for notching. Cut notches, then slide the platform back into place, install the top rails permanently and hook up the plumbing.

To fabricate the backrest, use 1/2″ plywood attached to the platform with two or three sturdy pieces of angle iron or "L's". Make the backrest overhang the rim of the hole by 1″ on all three sides so the rim can take up the sitter's weight. Upholster to taste.

The sink platform in the photo has been constructed with permanent searails to keep splashed water from running over all four sides. If you're a sloppy face washer, by all means emulate.

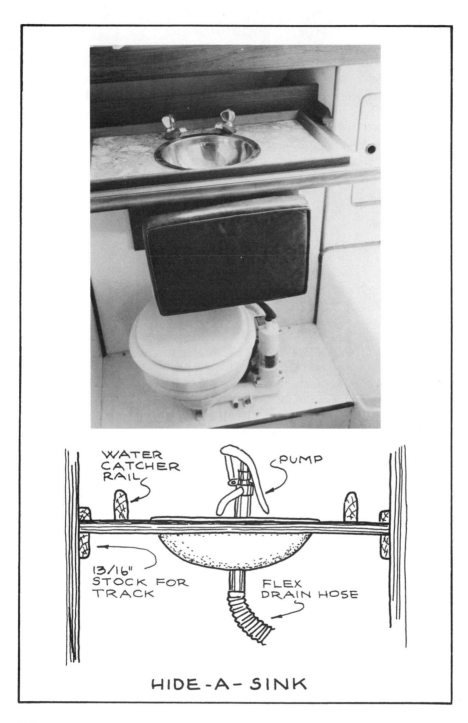

WATER
CATCHER
RAIL

PUMP

13/16"
STOCK FOR
TRACK

FLEX
DRAIN HOSE

HIDE-A-SINK

TOILET PAPER HOLDER

It's always sad to see a beautiful new yacht, spiffy and polished, well-outfitted in every detail, with a totally inappropriate chromed toilet paper holder streaking rust down a lovely white bulkhead.

Few fittings below are as vulnerable to salt as those in the head, since it seems to be common practice to leave the head portlight open for ventilation while the yacht is underway.

Consequently, toilet paper holders should be made of only brass, wood, or plastics. They should be small, so they're out of the way as much as possible; strong, so they can take the weight of misdirected bodies; and extremely easy to disassemble for roll change. If you're inclined to build Chinese wood puzzles, just take a deep breath, forget about it, and let the chrome monster run its streaks.

The following holder may be made of either wood or plastic. From 13/16" stock, cut two identical 3½" square pieces for the sides. Radius the outside corners well, or cut and curlicue to your heart's content. Three-fourths-inch in from the radiused front, centre and drill a 1/2" hole right through one piece, and half way through the other. Sand the edges so they don't splinter or chip. Cut two 6" long pieces of 1/4" × 3/4" stock, and let these into the backs of the sides 1/2" from top and bottom. Glue and screw with #6" flatheads. These bars will be used to mount the rack on a bulkhead.

From 1/2" dowel stock, cut a piece 5-5/8" in length, slip it through the through-hole, and into the half depth hole to fit. If it's too long, adjust now, for it must fit flush. Cut out a tear-shaped piece of brass, or thin rigid plastic, with the bulbous end 3/4". Drill a fine hole through the elongated part, just large enough to fit a small brass tack. Nail the tack to the side of the rack so the bulbous shape fits over the hole and keeps the dowel from slipping out. Paper roll change can be effected by slipping the dowl completely out of the hole, inserting the new roll, slipping the rod back into place, then sliding the flap shut to hold it there. Mount with four flat heads through the mounting bars, in a low spot, out of the way of hips and knees.

If a nearby locker has unused interior space, a very nice concealed mounting can be used. See "Concealed Paper Towel Holder" for details.

TOWEL RACKS

The major concern with towel racks is the material to be used. One should immediately eliminate the chromed atrocities from bathroom shops, for the chrome plating can be of an extremely poor quality that will chip and flake in a salt air environment. Solid brass racks can be found in shops that specialize in marine antiques, and we luckily found one from the *Queen Mary*. Brass racks from bathroom shops may be just plated, so beware.

Very fine racks can be fabricated once the material has been chosen. As lovely as teak is, it is a poor choice, for wet towels can cause it to mildew. Varnishing will, of course, help prevent this, so if you don't mind the upkeep, proceed. Cedar can be used to a most pleasing effect. For some reason, it seems to be more impervious to mildew than teak. The most ideally suited material, though, is clear plexiglass. It's easily workable, it looks very nice, and the cost of the material is most reasonable. A 1/2" plexiglass rod can easily span 18" without danger of breaking. The end blocks can be made of 3/4" stock, while the back can be 1/4" or less, or eliminated altogether.

Cut the two end pieces to 2½" × 1½", radius the front corners to eliminate nasty points, and, 1/4" back from the front face, drill a 1/2" hole about half way into the 3/4" plexiglass. Cut your rod to length, and glue it into place with plexiglass solvent. This last bit must be performed on a very flat, very even surface with the end blocks sitting squarely on their to-be-mounted sides, to insure that they will remain parallel for mounting.

At this point, a choice is to be made. If the back of the bulkhead or cabinet face, on which the rack is to be mounted, is accessible, then set the rack in place, mark the perimeters of the end blocks, and drill four pilot holes (two each) from the head side. Now, go to the other side of the bulkhead, and while someone holds the rack in place over the pilot holes, drill with a tapered bit into the rack, using the pilot holes as guides. Countersink the bulkhead, screw, and plug. If rear access is not available, a mounting plate of thin plexiglass will have to be used. Cut this to fit flush all around the end blocks, glue it onto them with solvent, and mount with four screws.

A note on placement. Do not put towel racks in a spot where sitters may be tempted to use them as hand rails, or if you must, install an unmistakable teak grabrail nearby.

TOWEL RACKS

FOLDING WASH BASIN

This is a pretty little Simpson Lawrence unit which comes totally assembled, ready to install. It's a perfect solution in small heads and even better on small boats where only a toilet exists. On large vessels, it provides tasteful and unobtrusive washing units in cabins. The basin is of high density plastic. Overall dimensions are a conservative 16″ high, 13½″ wide and when folded, only 6¼″ deep. The sink itself extends sufficiently when open that side access to it can be gained, so mounting can be done at 90° to the user if limited space so demands. Dumping the water is achieved by lifting the sink into its "folded" position. A tap (tap-shaped plunger pump) is available with the unit for about $20, but if you have a preferred unit, by all means use it. A simple soap holder is built in.

You will of course have to plumb it in yourself, providing a fresh or salt water intake and a waste outlet. Since additional seacocks are to be avoided at all costs, improvisation is in order. If the marine toilet is anywhere nearby, the task should be simple.

Waste

Since the outlet is for a 3/4″ hose, which usually is a manageable and discretely installable bit of tubing, the simplest thing would be to run the hose in a tasteful and tidy fashion between the hinged part of the seat and the bowl, terminating it just as it enters the bowl. A hoseclamp on the tubing as near the bowl as possible and screwed to a bulkhead or partition will do nicely to keep it in place. Admittedly you'll have to pump out the bowl every time you use the sink, but that seems a small price to pay for a "no-hole" in the hull. Besides, every toilet could use a nice soapy flush now and then.

Intake

A regular "T" takeoff from any part of the freshwater supply will do fine. If you're a freshwater-saver contemplating a salt water pump, the ideal thing to use would be a "T" takeoff from the toilet intake, *if* and only if the intake is *well forward* and *well above* the head outlet. Pumped effluent spreads over a great area; if you don't believe me, just look over the side next time you pump. If you're in doubt about the sufficiency of the locations of your intake and outlet, forget the whole thing and just tap into your freshwater system. Better to die a thousand times of thirst than to brush your teeth once with shee-shee.

FOLDING WASH BASIN

chart table/
navigation

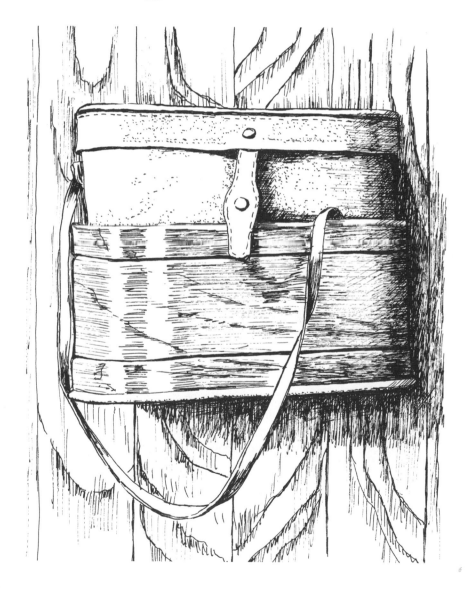

ENDLESS NOTE PAPER

This is a must. It is the handiest thing since the invention of toilet paper rolls. Using a roll of adding machine tape, and fabricating a holder for it inside a cabinet (see "Concealed Paper Towel Rack"), will give one an almost limitless supply of note paper.

The best location for it is in a high cabinet, near the chart table or galley. Here, notes can be left for oncoming crew, check lists can be written, and on lonely nights, yards of paper can be used up playing solitary tick-tack-toe.

Adding machine tape varies in width, so get the widest possible and cut a slit in the cabinet to suit, then, if you can't get the exact width in a Madagascari fishing village, to replace the roll, you can always get narrower stuff and make do.

Cut the slit with drill and jigsaw, then work the edges round and smooth by running folded sandpaper through. Next, fetch a piece of thin copper or brass sheeting and cut it to 6″ length. This will be your writing surface; without it the wood cabinet would be grooved with pen and pencil lines in no time. Make the width 1″ wider than the slit. One way to keep the paper flat against the writing surface is to cut two cross pieces from the brass stock and bend the edges under to allow space for the paper to slip through. Fit these to the upper and lower ends of the brass pad. Brass tacks through the ends of the cross pieces will be the only things needed to attach the whole rig to the cabinet. The lower cross piece can double as a tearing edge.

Mount the pad at least 1″ under the slit. If you mount it higher, you'll have a hell of a time feeding the new rolls through the brass guide.

If the pad is located away from the chart table, where writing utensils are always accessible, an elegant touch would be a single holed pencil holder fitted directly next to the pad. See "Pencil Rack."

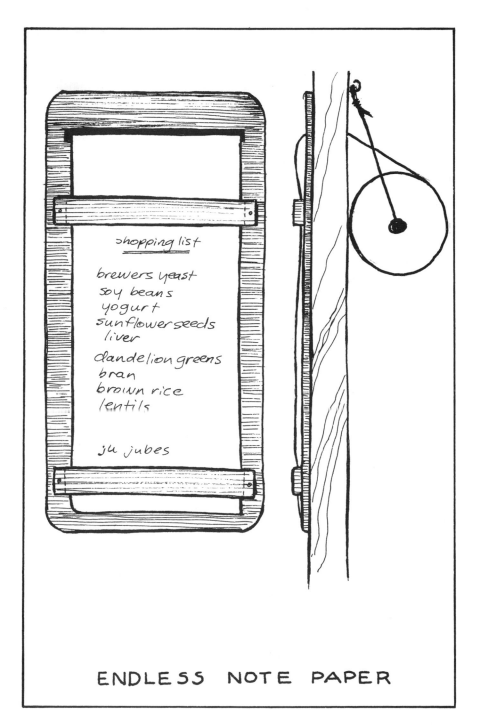

ENDLESS NOTE PAPER

HAND-HELD COMPASS STOWAGE

One of the most vital tools for coastal navigation, one which can get a fix on a vessel's position within one minute, is in many cases subjected to unnecessary abuse. This condition seems all the more preposterous when coupled with the reverence given to the fixed ship's compass. I'm not for a moment advocating that the main compass be mis-managed to create a more egalitarian state of affairs, I merely suggest that this delicate and costly instrument be given better treatment than being stuck in a feeble little metal bracket provided by the manufacturer. The bracket will, of course, provide sufficient bondage, but it still leaves the compass exposed to physical violence of all kinds. In short: box it.

The more pricey compasses do come with an optional box for about 40 modest dollars — usury at half the price. Construction of a tiny box takes no genius. If you are reluctant to get involved with a dovetailing jig, simply construct a butt-sided box from 1/4" stock. A 5" wide by 10" high by 4½" deep box will do for most compasses. To be totally accurate, make the interior of your box 1/2" wider than the widest part of your compass, the height 1" more including the prism, and the depth 1/4" greater. Thin plywood stock will do nicely for the back. Glue and brass tack the whole thing together.

Next, you'll have to fabricate blocks to hold the compass immobile in the box. Set the compass inside the box as perfectly aligned as possible to both axes. Measure for small blocks of 1/2" stock to hold the shoulders of the face *down*, and fit for a U-shape block of 3/4" stock to firmly accommodate the base of the handle. Don't be pompous, scrap bits of soft woods will do nicely here. Line all wood surfaces that will be making contact with the compass with thin self-adhesive weatherstripping, or felt. Once the compass is snugly in its home, find a point (somewhere at the joint of the handle and the base would be most ideal) where a 3/8" dowel can be slipped from side to side for support. Drill through one side from the outside, and continue with the drill bit half way through the next side. Cut a dowel to length to fit flush when inserted. From light gauge brass, cut a tear-shaped piece about 1½" × 1", pin it with a brass tack through the narrow part to enable the flap to pivot and alternately cover or expose the end of the dowel. Varnish the box inside and out. Mount the box with the open side facing aft to enable the compass to act as a course verifier down below. Now that loops shippy.

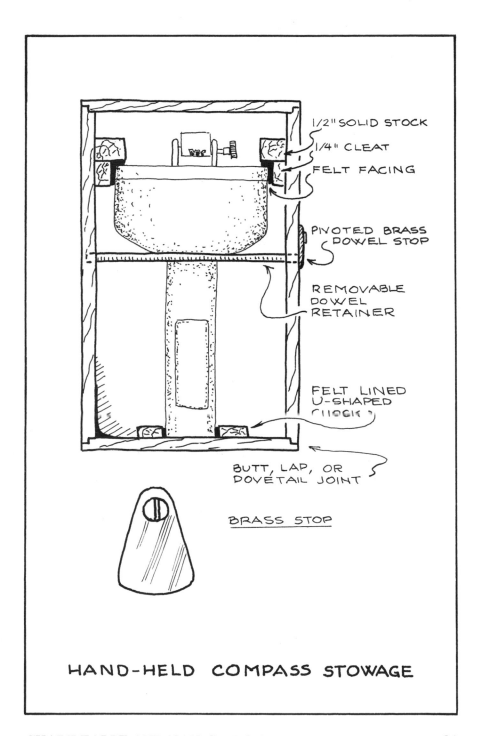

1/2" SOLID STOCK

1/4" CLEAT

FELT FACING

PIVOTED BRASS
DOWEL STOP

REMOVABLE
DOWEL
RETAINER

FELT LINED
U-SHAPED
CHOCK

BUTT, LAP, OR
DOVETAIL JOINT

BRASS STOP

HAND-HELD COMPASS STOWAGE

THE FLIP-UP CHART TABLE EXTENSION

A most commendable improvement in many recently designed yachts has been the inclusion of a chart table. By necessity, these have been allotted relatively small areas and more often than not, are of the sit down variety, frequently employing the foreward end of a quarter berth for the seat. This makes for a handy place to sit and work out navigation details and future trips, or fill in the log, but the small surface area of the table itself is the most inappropriate for actual chart work involving navigation tools and large charts. With the addition of a hinged extension, these severe limitations can be easily overcome.

If the chart table has its own independent seat, the solution is simplest, for then the back of the seat can support the hinged piece. This can be made of $1/2''$ teak or mahogany plywood with the appropriate trim on all sides. The trim must be flush top and bottom to avoid complications in either the stowed or engaged position. The prudent will affix the extension with a piano hinge, since occasional heavy pressure in the form of leaning bodies will be unavoidable. Securing the extension to the deck itself will not be such an enviably simple matter. Barrel bolts inboard and out do not provide sufficient support, and even if they did, their positioning would not be very hygienic. Knees hinging out from the aft face of the desk have been used with moderate success, their largest drawback being that they're rather unattractive when not in use. Possibly the most clever arrangement I've ever seen involves two sliding rods which stow fore and aft inside the desk. When required, they slip out through holes in the desk face (they themselves plug holes when not in use) and fit snugly into two corresponding holes in the back of the seat. This seems the least complicated of any system, requiring only two $1''$ dowels or similar sized stock, and a $1''$ hole cutter or a chisel.

If the desk is of the quarter berth add-on variety, the problems begin. The extension must be hinged from the hull itself. A $2''$ wide piece of $3/4''$ plywood, bonded to glass hulls or epoxied to wood ones, should be used as a base for the hinge. *Do not* screw anything into the hull. A tidy $3/4'' \times 3/4''$ cleat can be added to the aft face of the table to support the forward edge of the extension. The aft part can be supported by a hinged leg added on to the extension which can rest in an indentation on the inboard edge of the quarter berth.

With either extension, you'll be able to tackle any size chart without having to fold it to the size of a Sunday hankie.

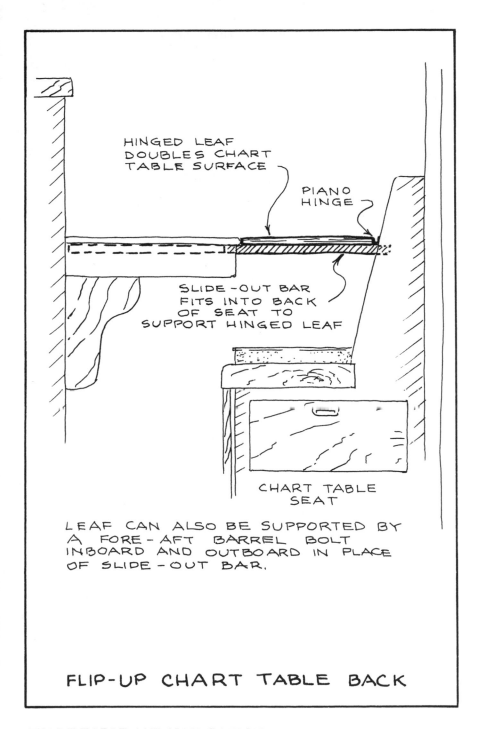

HINGED LEAF
DOUBLES CHART
TABLE SURFACE

PIANO
HINGE

SLIDE-OUT BAR
FITS INTO BACK
OF SEAT TO
SUPPORT HINGED LEAF

CHART TABLE
SEAT

LEAF CAN ALSO BE SUPPORTED BY
A FORE-AFT BARREL BOLT
INBOARD AND OUTBOARD IN PLACE
OF SLIDE-OUT BAR.

FLIP-UP CHART TABLE BACK

STOP WATCH HOLDER

An hour's work can produce a tasteful stop watch case from either plexiglass or wood, or a combination. Scrap pieces will do nicely since the case is small, exceeding the watch's diameter only by 1/2″ on three sides, and not at all at the top.

The case will be made of three layers. The thickness of the front and back can be 1/4″, while the centre piece need be just under the full thickness of the watch.

Cut the back to final size. Be sure the top is low enough to allow manipulation of the reset and "stop" and "start" buttons without the need of removal from the case. Cut the middle and front pieces to similar shape, then set them one at a time into a vise, and drill the following holes with hole saws. The hole in the thick middle piece should match the diameter of the watch, while the hole in the thin front piece should have the diameter of just the watch's crystal. This will make for a secure fit, yet allow total visibility of the face. It would be a mistake to leave the front piece solid plexiglass for then the face of the watch would rub constantly against it, scratching both surfaces to opaqueness. Now cut out the pieces above the holes to form a "U". Round off the edges of the holes in the front piece with sandpaper, then glue and clamp the three pieces together. When dry, finish off the edges with a file or sandpaper, depending how closely matched your pieces are. Mount with a single screw just behind the watch. Line it with felt.

If properly placed, high up within reach of the companionway, the navigator taking celestial shots will be able to use it safely, instead of having it dangle precariously from a lanyard around his neck. Using a sextant from the security of the companionway is in itself heartwarming, then simply one-fingering a firmly affixed stop watch, would make the process a dream. Since most navigation areas directly adjoin companionways, the watch can then be left untouched until the time is entered in the tables.

Besides, it looks professional.

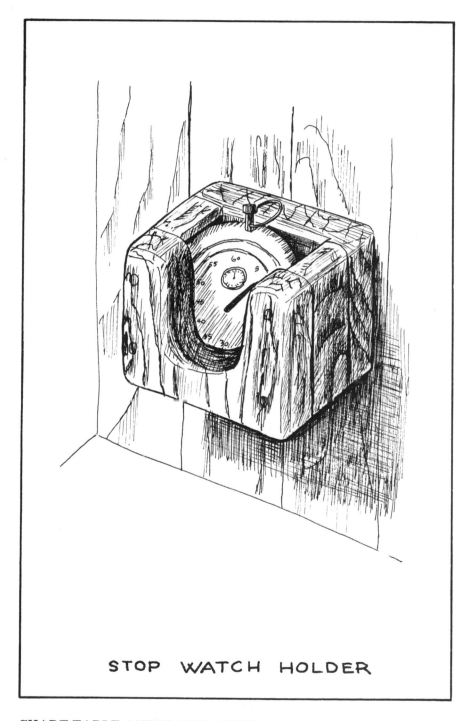

STOP WATCH HOLDER

RADIO RACK

One of the most precious pieces of equipment aboard any yacht is the radio receiver. Since most of the best ones, like the Zenith Trans-Oceanic, are of a design that somewhat resembles a portable transistor radio, the temptation to treat it as such is fairly hard to resist. As a consequence, the radio will be found lying all over cockpits, and foredecks and lockers, or wherever the whim of the music lover carries it. A great mistake. The radio should have a permanent and very secure place below decks from which it should not be moved, unless it's being used as a direction finder, or if reception in that particular position is insufficient and a new locale must be tried.

One basic rack design will function very well for most situations (see diagram). The only adjustment necessary depends on the amount of space available above the unit. If the rack will be simply attached to a bulkhead, then it can be made to be top loading, i.e. the rack will need to have no moving parts. If, however, the radio will be located directly below a shelf or the deck, then front loading will become necessary, entailing one hinged side and a removable frontal retaining bar.

Top Loading

Three pieces of 13/16" teak or mahogany should be cut: the bottom just 1/4" longer than the radio itself and about 2" wider. The two sides will be identical in width to the bottom and should have a height closely equal to that of the radio. If a side control exists as it does for band selection on the Zenith, a cutout somewhat larger than the control itself will provide access. The frontal support bar should be cut of the same stock to a width of no more than 1¼" or it will impede working of the front controls. Position the bar, quite high up, interfering with as few vital knobs as possible. Although end-screwing the bar through the sides would probably be adequate, a small routed or chiselled recess in the sides would give more security. The bar should be no more than 1/2" away from the face of the radio.

Assemble the parts as shown, using #10 1" S.S. P.H.S.M. screws. Countersink, glue and plug. To affix the rack to the bulkhead, hold the rack in place, draw a light pencil line around its bottom and sides, then remove rack, and drill pilot holes through the outlines. Three per side and three on the bottom should suffice. Have a friend hold the rack back over the outline and drill and screw from the

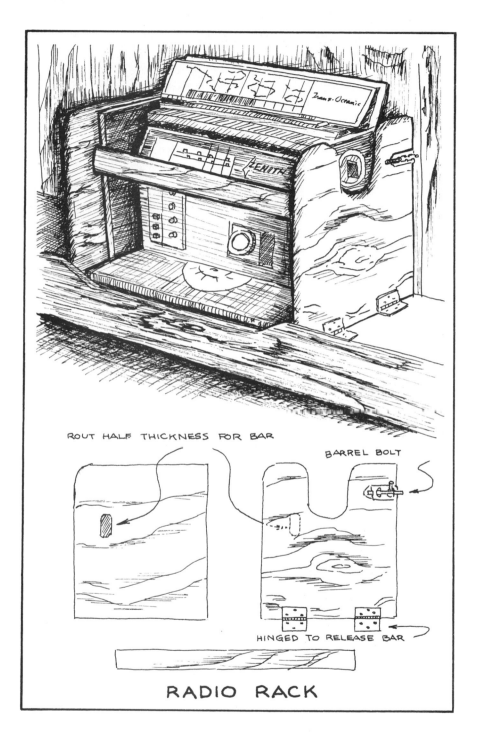

ROUT HALF THICKNESS FOR BAR

BARREL BOLT

HINGED TO RELEASE BAR

RADIO RACK

CHART TABLE AND NAVIGATION

other side of the bulkhead through the pilot holes. Use plastic resin glue and 1½" #10 P.H.'s.

For the front loading unit, mill the identical parts (bypassing the bottom, if the radio is to sit on a shelf or a counter) making sure you rout 3/8" deep recesses for the bar this time. Install one side permanently, but fit the other side with two small hinges on its bottom (outside), and a barrel bolt at the top to hold it in its vertical position. This side can then hinge down so the bar can slip out and the radio be removed.

Happy listening.

OVERHEAD COMPASS

A must for single handers, and a nice bit of luxury for others on passages of any length, is an overhead compass. Catalogues recommend "fixing above the owner's bunk to observe how the yacht is heading," in other words, to make sure the helmsman hasn't skipped off to the rum locker.

Whatever the excuse required, it would be pleasant to be able to glance up in a half-sleep and, without actually disturbing one's dreams, verify the ship's heading, then quickly return to matters of greater import. The sensible size of this bit of decadence should be, of course, *small*. The most commonly used ones seem to be rather bulky — 4½" high and over 8" in overall diameter — which I fear would be more of a skull-cracker than a mind-settler. But if you have height over your bunk and money in your pocket, by all means indulge. What the hell, you only live once.

OVERHEAD COMPASS

NAVIGATION TOOL BOX

This is another item most requisite on small yachts where a regular chart table with its wanted drawers is spacially uneconomical, but it's a beautiful thing on any yacht. It is essentially a $14'' \times 3'' \times 3''$ box with a hinged drop front (much like the overhead chart cabinet but on a smaller scale) constructed to accommodate pencil lead, parallel rules, pencil sharpener, erasers, and for those unwilling to construct a proper stop watch case, a stop watch.

Three-sixteenth inch stock is needed to house the screws and the hinge, but a thin $1/4''$ piece will nicely suffice for the back. The top, bottom, and sides should be butted and screwed, or dovetailed and glued, while the back can be brass tacked and glued, since it will not be visible anyway. The solid drop door should be bullnosed. Note that the piece for the front covers all end grain of top, sides, and bottom. A $7/8''$ or $1''$ finger hole should be drilled and bullnosed. Small butt hinges should be let into both drop door and bottom edge with a very small $3/8''$ chisel for a perfect fit. Because of the lack of weight in this door, even the hated bayonet snap-lock should be sufficient to keep it tightly closed in most conditions. To attempt installation of the more positive locking, finger-tripped elbow catches in such a tight space would prove to be a challenge, even to those well-versed in building brigantines in bottles.

A searail $1/2''$ high would be a nice touch just inside the door to a) keep things from falling out when the door is open, and b) prevent things from rolling between the hinges when the door is being closed. The latter could easily rip out the small hinge screws.

One small note. You'll realize I mention storage for pencil leads. We have constantly found the reloadable draftsman's pencil superior to ordinary ones. First, if the lead snaps, a flick of the finger will bring on a new tip without the lengthy interruption of pencil sharpening. Second, avoided are the horribly stubby creatures one inevitably ends up with, that are too short to sharpen, too short to store, and too short to find. A pair of draftsmen's pencils are a solid investment, especially if neatly stored in a pencil rack. Oh yes. For the less ambitious who store their stop watches here or other sublet areas; sew the poor thing a little pouch out of scrap leather. The crystal will remain legible much longer.

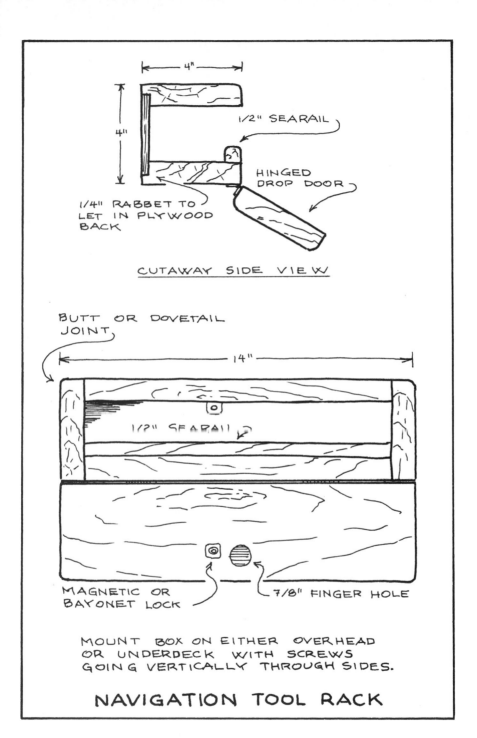

4"

4"

1/2" SEARAIL

HINGED
DROP DOOR

1/4" RABBET TO
LET IN PLYWOOD
BACK

CUTAWAY SIDE VIEW

BUTT OR DOVETAIL
JOINT

14"

1/2" SEARAIL

MAGNETIC OR
BAYONET LOCK

7/8" FINGER HOLE

MOUNT BOX ON EITHER OVERHEAD
OR UNDERDECK WITH SCREWS
GOING VERTICALLY THROUGH SIDES.

NAVIGATION TOOL RACK

DEPTH SOUNDER BRACKET

Great controversy boils over the ideal location of depth sounders. The new digital types with succinct bright numbers can be placed in the cockpit, totally ideal indeed for the helmsman steering in a fog by the fathom lines, or doing tight navigation in foreign ports, but this leaves a void down below for the navigator who has to work at night.

A good compromise with any sounder (especially with the traditional ones which must be kept out of the weather) is the hinged mount. This can be focused in or out, serving double duty.

A block of 13/16" teak is ideal, cut and decorated to match the boat's personality, and hinged on a sturdy brass or stainless piano hinge. Mount the sounder on this block, and attach a smaller block to the cabin side, and affix the hinge between them. Make sure your mounting block has enough room beside the sounder to clear the trim around the companionway. Since a lot of play will be required in the wires, the best solution is to use a piece of coil cable, such as found on telephone receivers. Two sets of hooks and eyes are needed. One at the unhinged end with the eye in the pad and the hook in the cabin side to fix the bracket for use down below; the other at the hinged end with the eye (the smaller obstruction) in the companionway trim and the hook on the hinged pad to hold it in the open position for cockpit use.

Companionway positioning is admittedly awkward, endangering life and instrument, so a preferred alternate would be to install a small portlight in the aft face of the cabin and hinge the sounder in front of it for cockpit use. Whatever the location, make certain that the read out face is always shielded from the sun, for (especially on the traditional spin types) the soundings are virtually impossible to read in direct bright light.

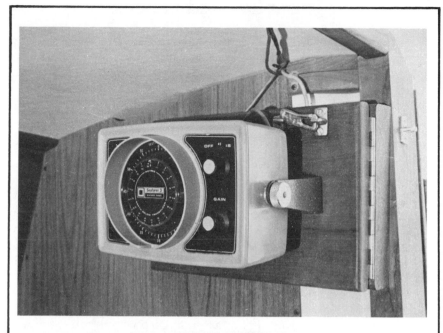

DEPTH SOUNDER BRACKET

OVERHEAD CHART RACKS

In many small yachts where no space is available for large chart drawers, the traditional leaning has been toward stuffing charts under bunk cushions; a totally needless venture into decadence. Ample unused space is available overhead, and two very simple stowage bins can be constructed, one for "folders" and one for "rollers". Both schools have reasons for their madness.

For Rollers

This is actually a magnified pencil rack. Three-quarter-inch stock can be used, ripped to 4″ widths, with 3″ diameter holes cut with a hole saw on the centrelines. The length of the rack and the number of holes depend on the amount of space available. Do not attempt to drill smaller holes. Rolling a chart tighter than 3″ will lead only to prolonged wrestling matches. One advantage of this rack is the potential for exterior markings at the bottom of each chart hole. If you're using the same ten charts year after year, you could get really fancy and have tiny brass plates made up with the name of each chart engraved. Now that's decadence!

Mount the racks about 20″ apart in a place where you can easily reach the outboard piece of the rack. You'll need to, to thread some rambunctious charts that have a tendency to unfurl.

For Folders

A very tidy, flat, suspended chart box can be made out of a piece of 3/8″ plywood slightly larger than a twice folded chart, and 3″ wide solid 13/16″ stock. If you want it to look beautiful, fit the back of the box flush against the curve of the cabin sides. Cut the plywood to width and rough cut to maximum needed depth, i.e. be sure to have the short side cut at least as long as the longest folded chart. Add to this the difference of cabin curvature over the width of the box to arrive at the rough length of the long side. Fit as close as possible with the inboard end running parallel to the keel. Scribe it with a compass from end to end with the pencilless tip on a constant line of the cabin side (on a constant vertical plane). You've got your curve. Cut with a jigsaw on a slight bevel to match the slope of the sides. Use the same angle to cut your 3″ wide frame ends. Fit the sides on and glue and screw into the plywood at 12″ centres. Mount on overhead with glue and screws. Don't drill or screw right through the cabin top. If you can mount it against a deck beam, so much the better. Use two simple butt hinges on a piece of solid stock cut to 3″ width to make up a drop door. Secure the door with a barrel bolt.

THE FINELY FITTED YACHT

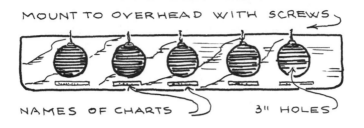

MOUNT TO OVERHEAD WITH SCREWS

NAMES OF CHARTS   3" HOLES

DIAGRAM A
CHART RACK FOR "ROLLERS"

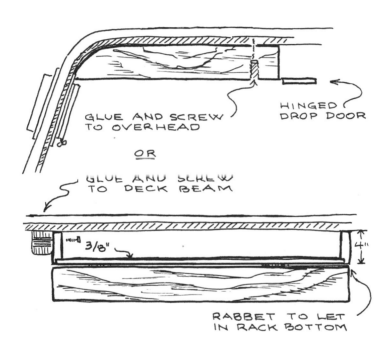

GLUE AND SCREW
TO OVERHEAD

HINGED
DROP DOOR

OR

GLUE AND SCREW
TO DECK BEAM

3/8"   4"

RABBET TO LET
IN RACK BOTTOM

DIAGRAM B
CHART RACK FOR "FOLDERS"

OVERHEAD CHART RACKS

SIGNAL FLAG RACKS

Signal flags are cute. They can be run up to celebrate arrival and departure of friends, as well as send messages in inconvenient moments, like the sinking of your ship. These little flags will prove totally useless if randomly stuffed and jammed into a sack or a drawer. Ready access to all flags is essential, and ready access to each specific flag at a specific time, without rummaging and searching and cursing, is mandatory.

Since each flag is clearly stamped with the letter or number it represents, stowage will have to be arranged so each of these stamps is clearly visible. A set usually contains 40 flags: 26 for letters, 10 for the numbers, three repeats, and one for "code". When individually rolled with the stamps showing, each flag occupies a minimum space of $2\frac{1}{2}'' \times 2\frac{1}{2}'' \times 3''$ for depth. The total area needed for proper stowage need be no more than about $14'' \times 22''$, or any combination yielding 308 square inches.

The material should be solid, stock cut to $1/4''$ thickness and $3''$ width. Cut it to whatever length you've decided on. If unavoidable, $1/4''$ plywood can be substituted. At $2\frac{1}{2}''$ intervals, a $1/4''$ wide let in should be cut to one-half the depth, in this case $1\frac{1}{2}''$. Slide the pieces into each other until a honeycomb has been assembled. A touch of glue on each joint might be used for added security. Frame the whole thing in $1/4''$ stock. Butt the joints and glue and nail with brass tacks. Two small brass "L's" on top and bottom (inside the pigeon holes so they don't show) should be used to mount on bulkhead or whatever.

No door or outer covering is compulsory, especially if the rack is mounted athwartships. Neatly folded, the flags look very shippy and colorful nestled in their little homes.

THE FINELY FITTED YACHT

SIGNAL FLAG RACKS

MAGNIFYING GLASS HOLDER

You may frown upon esoteric yacht gear such as a custom fitted magnifying glass holder, but it's these fine details that ultimately distinguish a yacht from a pick-up camper or a wheelbarrow. The specific one in the photo adorns a bulkhead next to the chart table of *Wanderer IV,* and is used very frequently to discern chart details in unfavourable lighting.

One must begin by searching through antique shops to find a beautiful specimen of a classic magnifying glass. Next, cut a piece of solid stock down to the same thickness as the thickness of the handle, and width and length to border the handle by at least 1" at any point. Lay the handle upon the wood, draw its outline, then cut it out with a jigsaw. Lightly bullnose all edges and sand.

Next, from half-inch stock, cut a small piece (3/4" × 2½") with the grain running along the length, then drill a hole through its center so that a #10 flat head brass screw will turn in it, somewhat stiffly. Then, drill into the holder itself as shown, insert the screw, and tighten only to the point where the "lock" will still turn but not fall into a vertical position on its own. Now, slip in your magnifying lens and enjoy. If that's not shippy, I don't know what is.

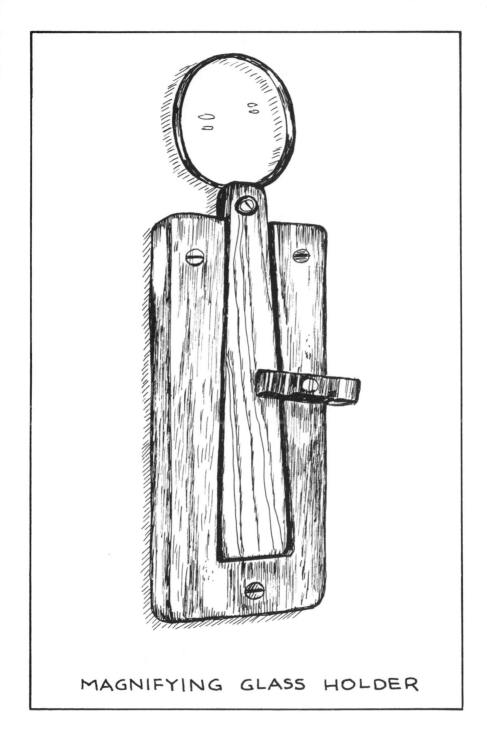

MAGNIFYING GLASS HOLDER

FLASHLIGHT AND FLARE RACKS

I feel that the presence of a flashlight very close to the companionway is mandatory, whether a yacht is to spend the night at sea or at anchor. Any emergency situation contains more than enough surprises without one's having to resort to little games like "flashlight flashlight, where is the flashlight?"

The bracket illustrated will not only guarantee protection and ready access to the flashlight, but it will also free some valuable shelf or drawer space. It requires a vertical space somewhat less than one and one-half times the light's length and only very slightly more than its width.

You'll require two square pieces of wood cut from 1/2" solid stock. Let the size be 1" greater than the diameter of the flashlight's handle to give you a 1/2" shoulder all around. Cut the mounting plates from similar stock to an identical width and 1½" height. Next, insert each bracket piece in a vise, mark the centrelines, and with a hole saw whose diameter is equal to that of the flashlight, cut completely through one piece and about two-thirds of the way through the other (to be the bottom piece). Now, butt one piece to each mounting plate and glue and screw with #8 P.H.S.M.S. Allow them to dry overnight. Install the brackets in such a way as to make sure the flashlight switch will not cause the flashlight to hang up on the upper bracket. Now that you have the bracket, make sure you use it.

The bracket for the flare is done in a similar fashion for a similar purpose. If a tapered hand flare is to be used, the best and simplest thing is the U-shaped bracket (see photo) that consists of two sides and a back. This has the advantage of taking a flare straight in, unlike the flashlight holder which requires much space above to allow the flashlight to be dropped in. If a flare gun is to be used, the bracket will, of course, be rather complex and designed to fit the individual gun, but, in either case, the location for the bracket is vital, for the flares should be kept safely out of both weather and traffic. The Hiscock's flare (see diagram) is stored both high and well back beneath the bridge deck, where it's accessible, but safe.

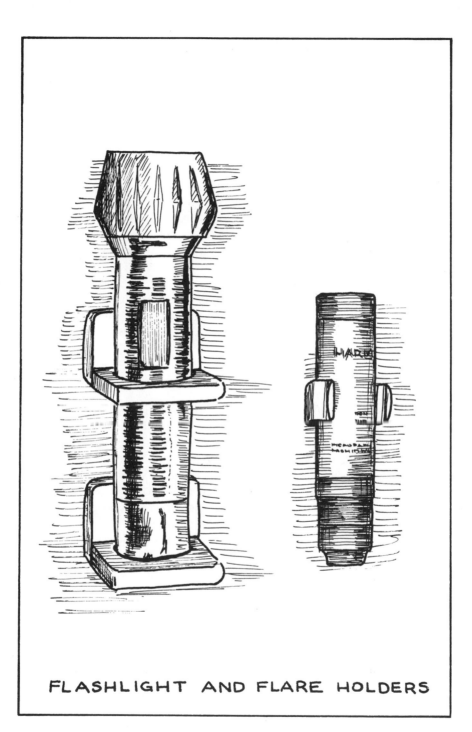

FLASHLIGHT AND FLARE HOLDERS

PENCIL HOLDER

This little critter is so painfully simple, I'm almost embarrassed to write about it; but here goes.

Rip a piece of 2″ by about 8″ long strip from 13/16″ stock of whichever wood you prefer. Remember *rip* means with the grain. Round the ends and edges with a file and sandpaper. If you want the rack to look more graceful, bevel the ends with a jig or bandsaw. Now, place the piece of wood with a 13/16″ × 8″ side up into a vise using flat scrap pieces of wood to absorb the toothmarks. Scribe a light centreline down the length of the long side and mark points on 3/4″ centres along it. At the 1/3 and 2/3 points, leave gaps for mounting screws. Leave the last 2½″ space for one-handed dividers. These have about 2″ diameter hinged necks. Mark for a hole 1¼″ from the end for the dividers. Drill all holes with a 3/8″ bit, but first read on.

Be certain to wrap a piece of masking tape around the drill bit 1¾″ from the tip, and *do not* press into the wood beyond that point. Few things look less sophisticated than a person of average intelligence placing a pencil in the top of a rack, only to have it slip immediately out the bottom.

Since your piece of wood is quite thin, be sure to sight straight down the top of your drill, and drill as vertically as possible. If you have access to a drill press, the above need for caution will be obviated.

With your holes drilled, turn the wood wide-face up in the vise, and draw a centreline along the length of it. Where you skipped spaces, mark and drill two holes in the centre of each half. Drill with a tight, tapered bit and counter-sink. These are for housing mounting screws. Now, take the thing out of the vise and rip it lengthwise into two 1″ wide pieces. Voilà. All your holes will line up.

Sand and detail completely before installing. Some people like to make a single piece rack about 3″ deep. This is not advisable. Frustration can reach its apex when one spends endless hours fishing broken pencils, or junior's hard-packed gob-balls, out of 3″ deep pencil holes.

Mount 2″ apart with a dab of glue behind each. If you mount them further apart, your pens with pocket pins will dangle feebly from the top bar.

PENCIL HOLDER

CHART TABLE LIGHT

There seems little doubt that the flexible gooseneck lamp, if well situated, is the most ideal chart table light. If mounted on the underdecks over the chart table, the neck will sweep over a 12″ arc and throw enough light to cover an 18″ square area very well at any given time. Its solid black hood keeps the light out of the rest of the cabin so as not to disturb the sleeping crew. Even more important is that most lights come with a slip-on red plastic sheath, that can be put quickly over the light bulb to protect the navigator's night vision.

The better goosenecks have an arrangement whereby the shade or cowl is retractable if a more general lighting is required. The mounting base usually contains the on-off switch. Mounting can be accomplished with two screws. If mounted under the side or aft decks, the neck of the lamp can be bent up out of the way to give free access to areas behind it. Most units are available for 12 or 24 volt systems.

If you feel these lights render insufficient light for things when you would like the whole chart table floodlit, then the *Solite* fluorescent lights might be a good idea. They are quite compact (13½″ × 2″ × 1¾″ deep), have very low current consumption, and what's extremely important, they have a circuitry that's protected to reduce radio interference. Available from Thomas Foulkes for about $15.00.

CHART TABLE LIGHT

BINOCULAR HOLDER

This is not merely a decorative item. It's a must. To spend a small fortune on good binoculars only to have them shuffled from shelf to drawers is madness. They will scratch and become unusable in little time. Keeping them safely stowed in their original cases which, in turn, will be hidden in some dingy hole shows similar mental instability, for need of binoculars is usually immediate and the elusive buoy with the vital number on it in a viciously shoal harbour will have been long swallowed by fog by the time you unearth and unpack your precious toy.

Since little direct force will ever be placed on the box (hopefully), 1/2″ thick teak should suffice. Twenty inches of an 8″ wide board will be plenty if cautiously cut, and eight #8 panhead sheet metal screws will be enough for fasteners.

Cut the wood to dimensions shown, remembering that this case is made for binoculars with 2″ diameter lenses and a fully-open width of 6″. If yours differ, adjust accordingly. Take care that you align the grain of the front piece with the grain of the bulkhead, or ceiling, or whatever you intend to mount it on. Nothing looks less thorough than criss-crossing grains. Butt, glue and screw all pieces, *after* the bullnosing has been completed with a router. Do not forget to rout a good 3/4″ diameter hole in the bottom piece to allow for cleaning. Don't make the hole any larger than that, or the small lens covers shall incessantly fall through and roll astray.

Space permitting, the best place for a binocular case is just inside the companionway, within easy reach of the helmsman. Mounting in the cockpit should be avoided under any circumstances, for lenses cake and smear in salt air (not to mention the metal parts corroding), and when the poor sailor on watch most dearly needs them, he will see nothing in the distance but streaky fog and fingerprints.

Interior placement should be on the aft ceiling (cabinside) and as high up (to keep dry) as possible, but not so high that you can't yank the thing out of the case without crushing most of your fingers against a deckbeam.

One last note. A binocular case should never be used as a handy storage bin for keys, or screws or bottle openers. Deep scratches in expensive lenses have caused more deaths to scratchors than all other binocular deaths combined.

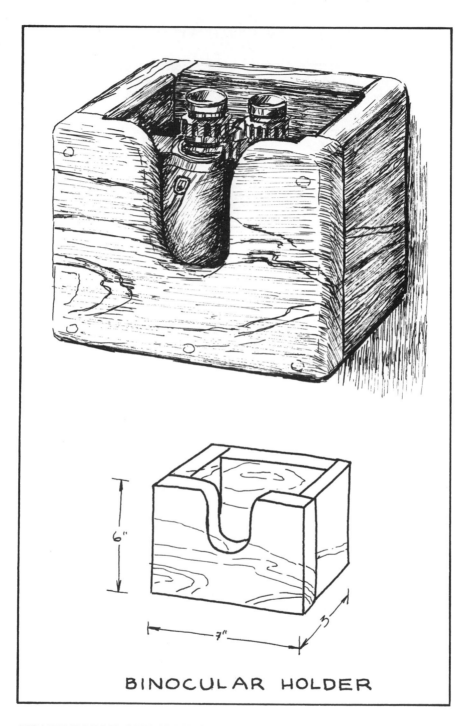

BINOCULAR HOLDER

SEXTANT/HAND HELD COMPASS MOUNTS

I was rather surprised once to see an expensive sextant aboard a yacht being stowed in a feeble tin bracket, exposed to dust and steam, on the excuse that the owner demanded quick access. Folly. The most secure place for a sextant is in the box designed specifically for it, and the most secure place for the box is on some nice protected shelf to which it can be securely screwed.

Susan Hiscock explained to me the additional importance of being able to work through the entire box-opening-sextant-removal operation with one hand when seas are rough and the yacht skittish. On these occasions, one hand will be required for survival.

To enable one to do this, a way will have to be found to hold the lid securely open so it will not come crashing down on the delicate mirrors and adjustment screws as the sextant is being removed. The sextant box will have to be located so that the open lid will be close to the hull on a bulkhead. Cut a 2'' long block to the thickness of your lid and fasten it to the bulkhead directly above the opened lid. Then with a single screw, loosely attach a small wood swivel (1/2'' thickness is plenty) to the block, and have this act as a lock to hold the lid open. The box latch can then be tripped with one hand, lid opened, swivel lock turned, and when the lid is secured, the sextant removed.

Hand Held Compass

A second compass aboard a yacht is most advisable. To risk the safety of crew and vessel on a single compass would be thoughtless. Many yachtsmen prefer a fixed back-up unit below decks so the yacht's course can be checked without venturing topsides. This seems a redundant expense. The better hand held compasses come in a very presentable wooden box complete with a little window and an external switch which, when flipped, places pressure on the finger trigger in the compass, illuminating it for night use. The box need only be screwed to a bulkhead or shelf (mounted fore and aft will save adding or subtracting 90°) and a perfectly functional fixed compass is now in operation. Care must be taken that no metal be located near the compass, or it will be helplessly thrown out of kilter.

Sextant box screwed to locker top for one-handed operation.

LEAD AND LINE

Depth finders are lovely little instruments that spin and flash or just coolly blink exact little electric numbers at you. I'm first to admit that they are an absolute joy to use and play with, but one should prepare for their unscheduled demise and not be in a helpless state of tears when it comes. Having a proper lead and line aboard can enable a crew to proceed just as safely, if not quite as conveniently. They worked wonderfully well for centuries so they should more than suffice in a modern emergency. Since chandleries that carry a lead-line are few and far between, one should undertake making his own.

First, either buy six pounds of scrap lead, or take the old dusty car battery from the corner of your garage and go at it with an ax (after having dumped out the very last drop of battery acid of course). Now get out an old pot you've always hated (actually a tin can will do just as well), put it over a hot flame, and throw in your lead, little by little. While it is melting, take two tomato paste tins (about 2″ diameter) and cut out the bottom of one and tape it with heavy duct tape to the open top of the other to form about an 8″ tube. Have nearby a galvanized eyebolt with a good 3″ stem and 1″ eye and you're ready for the fun. Set the tin tube up vertically using some rocks or bricks around it to make sure it won't tip and spill the spoils, then cautiously pour the molten lead into it. Fill it no higher than 1/2″ from the top, then quickly get hold of your eyebolt with a pair of plyers, and holding it by the eye, stick it into the molten lead until only the eye shows. Hold it there until the lead sets. When it's set, hammer off the tin can tube and voilà, you've got yourself one hell of a billy club.

Now fetch a 10 to 20 fathom line of about 1/2″ diameter (anything less will cut uncomfortably into hands) and splice one end of it to the eye, then, with careful measurements, mark in the fathoms according to the standard method which allows identification in the dark by feeling with hands or lips. These can be tucked into three-strand line or sewn onto a braid. Mark the first 10 to 20 feet with a simple marking for shoal water cruising.

The best method of stowing is to smartly coil the line and hang it in the rope locker on a piece of leather stripping (see "Rope Locker").

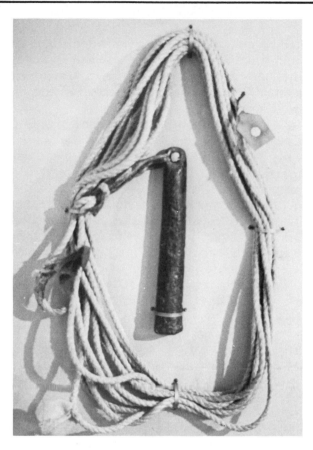

2 FATHOMS — LEATHER WITH TWO ENDS
(MARK TWAIN)
3 " — LEATHER WITH THREE ENDS
5 " — WHITE CALICO
7 " — COARSE RED FABRIC
10 " — FLAT LEATHER WITH HOLE
13 " — THICK BLUE SERGE
15 " — WHITE CALICO
17 " — COARSE RED FABRIC
20 " — CORD WITH TWO KNOTS

FATHOM MARKS

LEAD AND LINE

CHART SURFACE FOR CHART TABLE

This is such a clever idea that I'm surprised I didn't think of it myself. I found it on Ginny and Peter Marshall's beautiful Spencer. They are planning to cruise the Pacific Northwest for the next few years, so they laminated their most general chart of that area onto the surface of their chart table.

This should be done on most vessels, for not only does it look more attractive than vast expanses of formica or veneer, but it also provides wonderfully quick reference without searching through chart drawers and unfolding charts.

To laminate the chart, sand the existing surface lightly with 100 grit sandpaper, then take a *new* unfolded chart (anything with creases will be very difficult to laminate properly), and crop out the section you are most likely to use. Crop it so it fills the entire chart table surface from fiddle to fiddle. Do a dry run to make sure it's a perfect fit. Next, tape off around the area where the chart is to be laid, because you'll be using a spray adhesive and taping sure beats scraping. Now, take a can of said adhesive (available at most art and stationery stores), and spray the chart table surface judiciously, but evenly. With the help of a friend, hold the chart over the table and begin to lay it in place starting with one corner. Lay down only a 6″ square area at first, then press thoroughly to work out all air bubbles. From here on, lay the chart in inch by inch pressing firmly and thoroughly as you go.

When you're done, wipe the chart well and, without removing the surrounding masking tape, lay on two or three coats of satin finish varnish (the high gloss would throw too many reflections and would be more slippery), allowing sufficient time to dry between coats. A light sanding with 400 grit between coats would yield the best results.

When you decide to do extended cruising in a new region and feel that a new general chart would be of more use, you can easily replace the existing one by either peeling it away or better still, just leaving it and laying the new one over it in a similar fashion. It will be sometime before your accumulation of charts reaches the tops of the fiddles.

CHART SURFACE

salon

THE FINELY FITTED WET LOCKER

It strikes me as somewhat droll that most designers create a vertical space of about 48", slap a door on it, and call it a wet locker. And indeed these places live up to their name, for whatever you put in them will stay forever soggy and dank. Well, maybe not forever, just until they mildew. Apart from the physical space required to hang one's foul weather gear and stow one's boots and harnesses, three vital points must be considered and wet lockers modified accordingly. These are drainage, ventilation and proper stowage.

Drainage

Gear will have difficulty drying if it must forever dangle in its own drippings. In a fiberglass boat with a built-in liner, a small plastic through-hull should be fitted into the low spot of the locker and a hose led back into the bilge. As a further precaution, a grate can be installed in the locker to encourage passage of water away from the gear.

Ventilation

Surprising as it may seem, neither a small finger hole nor even a cut out in the shape of a tiny anchor in the door of a wet locker, will provide sufficient air circulation to dry clothes quickly. The most sensible solution is to replace the door provided with one having a cane insert. An alternate step and one perhaps more easily effected, would be to cut a very nice hole out of any part of the bulkhead that makes up the locker. This must be cut with great care and the edges thoroughly bullnosed. The corners can be radiused for a nice finished effect. The same caning can now be installed from the inside of the locker, using 1/4" stock for securing and trimming. Some people advocate drilling holes in a pattern. Unfortunately these do not provide sufficient air circulation and seldom look any better than what they are: a bunch of holes.

Proper Stowage

Plastic hangers should be used for all clothes. Rust stains on foul weather gear look very unsightly. Shallow shelves of netting should be installed so boots and gloves and hats don't sit in a hopeless soggy heap on the bottom of the locker. Wooden pegs (dowels) about 1¼" long can be used on 45° angles to provide space for safety harnesses. Use no cup hooks or metal fasteners in a wet locker. Expensive foul weather gear can be needlessly torn by such an oversight.

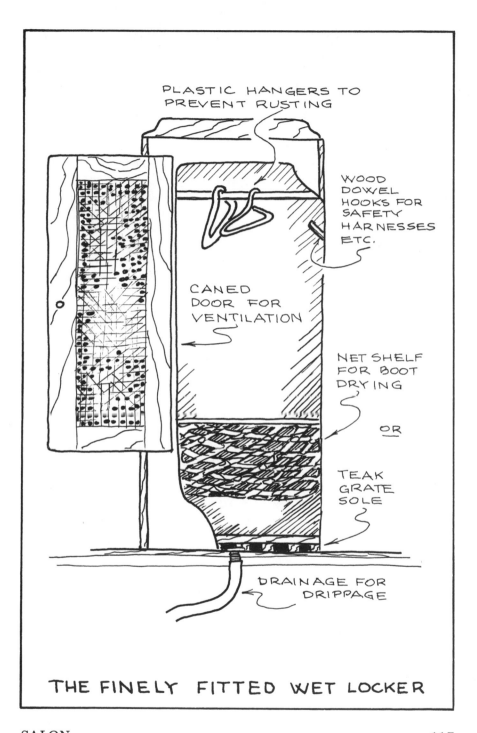

PLASTIC HANGERS TO PREVENT RUSTING

WOOD DOWEL HOOKS FOR SAFETY HARNESSES ETC.

CANED DOOR FOR VENTILATION

NET SHELF FOR BOOT DRYING

OR

TEAK GRATE SOLE

DRAINAGE FOR DRIPPAGE

THE FINELY FITTED WET LOCKER

GIMBALLED FLOWER POT HOLDER

All people who live aboard and most people who spend a lot of time on their boats like to have at least one live plant, but are usually deterred by the constant dirt sweeping and replanting which follows most sailing trips, unless they take place in an aquarium. A rather sophisticated looking, but basically simple-minded device, can be fabricated to keep the plant swinging, but in place. Granted, the pot will have to be small, about 4″ in diameter, basically eliminating your average palms and redwoods, but nicely accommodating bonsais or herbs. You'll have to go first to your local plumber and with a straight face, ask for a 3/4″ *length* of 4″ copper pipe and two 3/4″ lengths of 4½″ pipe. He'll mutter and curse, but he'll cut them for a nominal cutting charge on his magical pipe cutter.

Take home your treasures and drill two holes on opposite sides of the smaller ring and four holes on opposite sides of the larger ring. Cut a slit in the second large ring, and bend it into a "U", with a 5″ diameter mouth. Drill a hole in each end and one in the centre. Assemble the three rings with small flat head bolts and shallow nuts as shown in diagram. Use nuts as spacers. You will now have a double gimballed pot holder that will spill nothing and hit nothing. To attach, bolt through the centre of the "U" and back it up with a nice sized plate or washer. If through-bolting isn't possible, flatten the belly of the "U" and drill three holes in the pattern of a triangle, and attach with sheet metal screws.

Happy gardening.

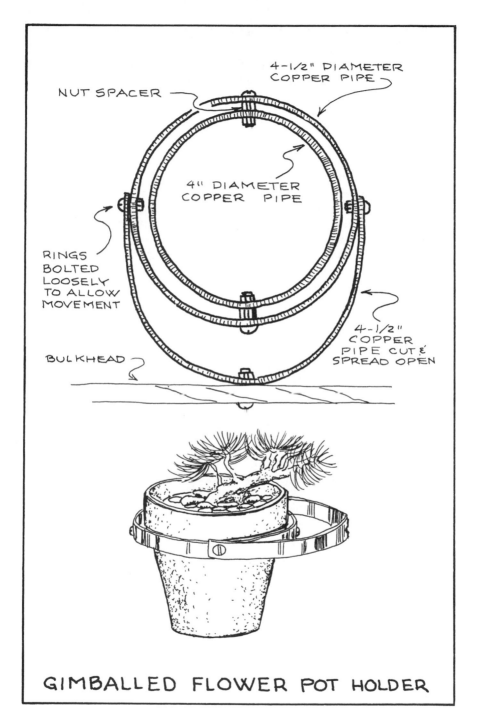

GIMBALLED FLOWER POT HOLDER

MAGAZINE RACK

They're everywhere. *New Yorkers* and *Elles* and magazines about sailboats and magazines about sailplanes clutter *Warm Rain* as if she were a used book shop. I throw out piles daily, but the publishers keep printing and Candace just keeps bringing. What can I do? All I can do is built racks to contain the beasts.

Fortunately, this is a fairly minor project, but one that will reap reward year after year, rag after rag.

The first thing to do is to find a nice flat vertical surface about 10″ × 12″ upon which the rack can be installed. Next, track down a 10″ × 9″ × 1/2″ piece of teak, or whatever you wish to use, and get two matching pieces for the sides about 3½″ × 9″. Be sure all your grain runs vertically. A piece of 1/2″ plywood will do for the bottom, unless your rack will be located up high so the bottom will show, in which case you'll need another 3″ × 10″ piece of stock. Cut the sides and the face with 45° angles where they are to meet. One-half-inch from the bottom, rabbet both sides and the face to let in the bottom piece. Assemble everything dry and measure the exact interior distance between the sides, then cut a dummy piece from scrap to fit. Now, glue all joints and assemble, slipping the dummy in at the unsupported top of the rack. Clamp with a short bar clamp to hold the sides and two C clamps to hold the face to the bottom piece and also to the dummy piece. Let set overnight.

In the morning, bullnose all edges and sand and oil or varnish. If you have done a good job, the rack will seem to have been hewn from a solid block of wood. If possible, mount on bulkhead or cabinet face by drilling and screwing into the sides from behind so the face of the rack can remain unmarred. Oops, almost forgot: drill a good 3/4″ hole in the bottom for cleaning.

Upon installation, you'll realize two things. One, the titles of most magazines will be visible over the rack; two, the rack holds only about ten magazines. If more than that find their way aboard, just store them carefully behind the companionway in a little container marked "garbage."

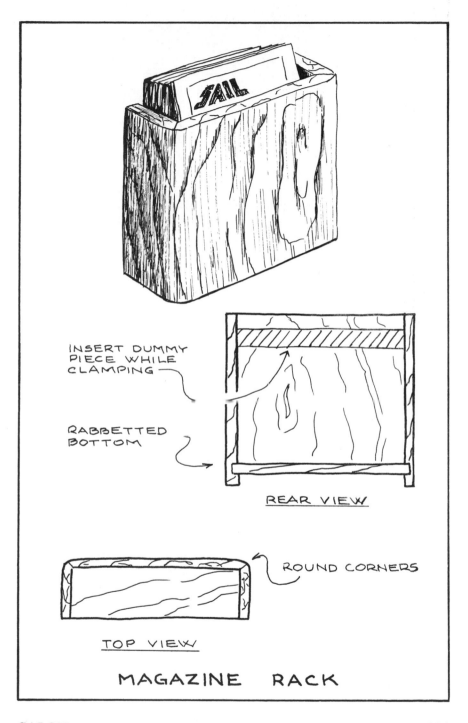

INSERT DUMMY PIECE WHILE CLAMPING

RABBETTED BOTTOM

REAR VIEW

ROUND CORNERS

TOP VIEW

MAGAZINE RACK

OVER BUNK FOOT LOCKER

When you're a crew on someone else's yacht, it's difficult to feel totally at home unless you receive your own cabin, an event which occurs seldom to never. The next best thing is your own bunk. It can feel so much more personal if it has above the foot a nice little locker where a few of your more precious things can be kept. The locker need not be enormous, indeed it is limited in height by the proximity of the deck, since, in most cases, we are speaking of quarter berths and pilot berths and bunks in the forepeak and aft cabins.

Their use should not be limited to visiting crew. Since each member of the family usually frequents the same bunk, a very private locker would seem a most useful idea.

Even over the narrowest bunk of 20", having a clear vertical space of only 24", a very neat little locker of 10" in height, 20" in width, and 16" in depth can be built. The opening should be fore and aft to keep things from slipping out.

The first 5" against the hull must of course be dedicated to books. Without books, there can be no civilization. This space should be no more than 6" deep, which of course means that there will be a bizarre area behind it, but that can be accessible with a little arm bending. This should be fitted with a half height baffle, and it will then hold a miraculous number of socks and underwear. Granted the sweaters in the adjoining area would have to be removed, but then, that's life. If you want lots of open space, move to the moon. The central area should be free for things like the aforementioned sweaters, but the last 5" should be saved for two 4" × 4" × 16" deep drawers, one above the other. Nothing holds tiny knickknacks from watches to razors to strange metal things you find on the beach and have to keep, better than a drawer, especially if it's divided into fore and aft sections.

The top and bottom and outboard side of the locker can be of 1/2" plywood, the inboard side of teak or mahogany. The locker will be too large to survive on butted joints alone, so cleat stock must be used where any large pieces meet others. Cleat stock will be needed along the underdecks to suspend the sides and partitions of the locker. The drop door should be of teak, equipped with a bayonet catch and a brass chain stopper. Doors and drawers should have 1" finger holes as handles. Sand and bullnose everything. Do a nice job. This little item will bring ooh's and ah's from even the coldest hearted visitors.

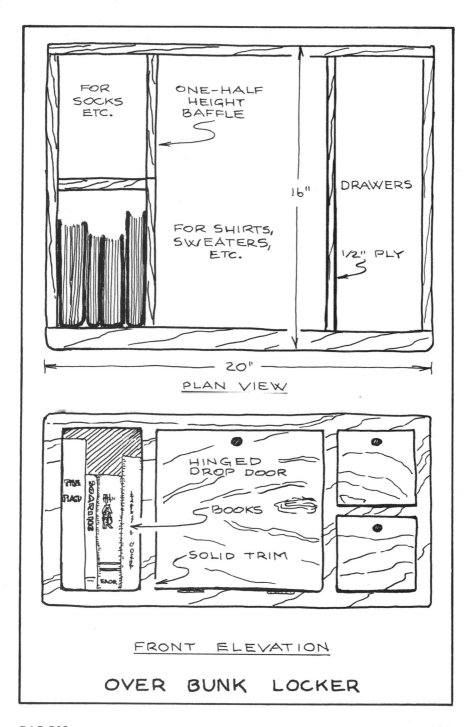

FOR SOCKS ETC.

ONE-HALF HEIGHT BAFFLE

FOR SHIRTS, SWEATERS, ETC.

16"

DRAWERS

1/2" PLY

20"

PLAN VIEW

HINGED DROP DOOR

BOOKS

SOLID TRIM

FRONT ELEVATION

OVER BUNK LOCKER

BOOK SHELVES

A yacht without books is a sad place indeed. Apart from the basic almanacs, pilots and scattered reference books, a goodly library is needed.

Size

Since most books today are leaning toward a standard 6″ X 9″ measurement, one major set of shelves can be based on these dimensions, adding an inch vertically to allow one book to be lifted over the searail without disturbing the others. The minimum depth should exceed 6″ by about 1/2″ and no more. The tighter the book fits behind the rail, the better.

A second shelf should be designed for paperbacks. These are totally standardized in the publishing industry to 7 1/8″ X 4¼″. Again, allow a spare 1″ vertical space and 1/2″ horizontal space. A large area should be left open for the above mentioned almanacs, sight reduction tables and loose-leaf binders. Most of these measure 10″ X 12″.

Quantity

Any available space should be made into book shelves. If they go unused, other items can be kept on them, such as recording barometers, transoceanic receivers, VHF radios, etc.

Location and Construction

Ideally, book shelves should be built athwartships, for then the need to hold them in place with lines, chains, or bars will be eliminated. The appearance of most bulkheads will be enhanced by orderly book shelves. See photo.

The most aesthetically pleasant shelves are those let either partially or totally into the bulkhead. These have the basic advantage of not depriving the main salon of space, and, in addition, most of the construction can be of inexpensive 1/2″ plywood since the bulk of it will be located in the head or forepeak or whatever it adjoins.

Determine your goal and make the bulkhead cutout. Construct a plywood box with a matching sized opening and let in 1/2″ plywood shelves. Assemble with 3/4″ radiused cleat stock on the *outsides*. This will hide the cleat from the main salon as well as make the box look less boxish from the other side. Trim the opening with "L" trim of teak or mahogany, or, if the bulkhead is painted, simply bullnose the edge of the opening and paint it without trim. An accent will be provided by the searails.

One important point: when milling your searails for shelves, be sure to make the rabbet at least 1/4" higher than the shelf itself. See diagram. This way the searail can overhang the shelf, and when screws are inserted, it will not split as it would almost surely do without the extra 1/4".

If delicate "L" trim is to be installed, finishing tacks should be used instead of screws. These will have to be drilled for as well, but you will not run as great a risk of splitting the wood as you would with even the smallest screw.

Fore and aft bookshelves are, of course, more simple to construct since the space is usually already defined by the hull and bulkhead, and cabinets, requiring only installation of a shelf, a searail, and some magical means of keeping the books in place.

Scribe and fit the shelf and install. Do not use cleat stock. That entails extra work and it looks messy. Attach the shelf by screwing through cabinet and bulkhead into the shelf ends. The same can be done with the searail, eliminating plugging. Glue everything well; you'll need the strength. If your shelf exceeds 20" in length you'll need a knee beneath it for additional support. This will have to be of solid wood. Scribing and fitting of the knee should be done before installation of searail.

For the fore and aft shelves, some method of keeping the books in place must be arranged. Some people suggest shock cords, but I find the idea quite impractical for unless the cord is absurdly taut, it will stretch and the books will dive effortlessly over it onto the cabin floor. The following three solutions seem to be reasonable in function and amount of work involved.

Brass Chain

Attached to padeyes on either end, brass chain works very nicely. The two end links will have to be bent so the chain will be taut yet removable without broken fingernails.

Wood Rods

A simple 3/4" dowel rod or 3/4" teak bar slipped into U-shaped wood chocks will do nicely and can be stored behind the searail when in port.

Hinged Searail

This is the most complex of the three, requiring a 4" high bottom hinged drop board. With a barrel bolt at either end, it provides very nice support, but it seems to be a bit too much work for what it accomplishes.

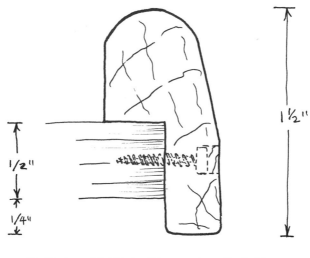

BOOKSHELF SEARAIL

1 1/2"

1/2"

1/4"

TABLE TOP STOWAGE

Whether your salon table is of the dinette or dropleaf variety, valuable storage space is probably being lost just below its surface. Most dinettes are wide enough to have a shallow 7″ wide box run down their spine and almost all dropleafs can facilitate the same.

This size stowage would do nicely for placemats, cutlery, serviettes, salt and pepper, etc., enabling attainment without leaving the table.

The first step is to decide the size of the box. Take into consideration under-table hardware and, more importantly, knee space. No one can have a pleasant dinner leaning over the table from a distance like a crane, so if your table is too narrow for both the box and knees, let the knees reign. Boxes can live elsewhere, but knees can only thrive on legs.

Once you've decided on the size, build the box of 1/2″ plywood with internal cleat stock. At this point, assemble only the four sides. In the bottom piece, drill a 1/2″ hole (to serve as a cleaning outlet) for each compartment that you plan. Affix the bottomless box in place to the underside of the table with cleat stock.

Measure in and outline the size of the lid you'll be cutting out of your table top, being sure you leave 1/2″ all around the inside perimeter to which you'll be attaching seating cleats that, in turn, will support the lid. See illustration. From below, drill four 1/8″ pilot holes in the corner of your drawn outline to establish the corners on the top where you will be doing your cutting. Cut out the lid most precisely with a hack saw blade and a jigsaw. Round all fresh edges with a very fine file and sandpaper.

The best, as usual, is left for last. Select a beautiful piece of solid 3/4″ wood for your lid. If your table top is dark, pick something light like ash or oak or maple; if it's light, use teak. Place the piece over the hole and, from below, scribe in the shape, then cut it. Cut your seating cleats to 1″ widths from 3/8″ plywood. Screw and glue them around the perimeter from below. If your table top is less than 3/4″ thick you'll have to rabbet your edges of the lid to fit. Mark the amount to be removed from underneath by running a pencil along the seating cleat. *Now* you can install the bottom of the box. Drill a 1″ diameter finger hole in the lid for a handle and enjoy.

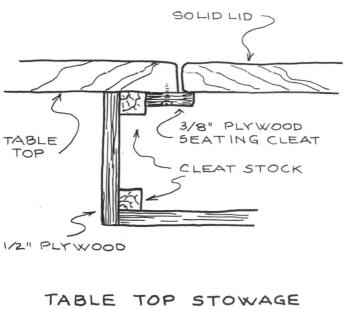

SOLID LID

TABLE TOP

3/8" PLYWOOD SEATING CLEAT

CLEAT STOCK

1/2" PLYWOOD

TABLE TOP STOWAGE

OPEN FOOT LOCKER

Most salons with a centre table arrangement tend to have full length berths running fore and aft. Many of these are never fully utilized as seats, for seldom are there six to eight people in a salon perched along them; thus, a great amount of valuable storage space is lost.

A very simple conversion can be made, requiring only three pieces of plywood, some cleat stock, and a bit of searail. This structure will provide an open locker for pillow and bedding, and a fine flat surface for mounting anything from a small stove to a moose head.

The dimension of the structure will depend on the layout of your boat and what sort of additional space you require. On *Warm Rain*, the main bulkhead extends clear to the mast support post, so we decided to run our foot stowage about 14" past the face of the berth, and create a top loading locker for wood and coal.

The top of the locker should be cut to about a 12" width, and whatever length you desire. The foot hole portion will need to be 13" high for large feet, plus 1½" to accommodate cleat stock and searails.

To join the two vertical plywood pieces together, mill a teak corner post (see "Desk" for details). Cut and fasten needed lengths of cleat stock onto the settee back and bulkhead, to form supports for the face and the top. Cut and attach cleat stock to the top edge of the face to form the last piece of foundation for the top. Glue and screw the face to the settee back, then glue and screw the top onto the fixed cleat stock. In both cases, try to do all the drilling and screwing from the inside, that is, from the cleat stock into the plywood, to avoid as much plugging as possible. If you are building a front loading cabinet, install all shelves *now* before you install the fore and aft cabinet face, then cut the face to fit, furnish with the cleat stock and fix into place. For door construction, see "Cane Doors." It's time to install the searails. If you wish to use traditional corner pieces, see "Searails Corners"; if not, read on. Get a piece of stock searail, slip it over the top of your new locker, mark for length, and cut on a 45° angle. Now, install this piece permanently in place. Take a rough-cut short piece of searail and mark on its face the distance between the bulkhead and the tip of your freshly cut 45° piece. Mark, cut, and install. Trim the foot hole with "L" trim. Paint or oil.

OPEN FOOT LOCKER

NON-SLIPPERY COMPANIONWAY RUNGS

Some companionways, be they ladders or removable steps, seem to come perfectly varnished and perfectly slick; ideal for slipped disks. Four very simple antidotes to ladder diving exist:

Macrame Pads

This is probably the most charming of the available ideas, doubling as a dirt catcher as well. Two fine examples made of hemp or old dacron, are the Flemish coil mat and the ultimate Ladder Step Mat. Their construction is wonderfully described in Harvey Garrett Smith's "The Arts of the Sailor," a fine book on rope work written 25 years ago that no mariner should be without.

Permanent attachment of any mat would be a mistake. Small bits of Velcro should be sewn beneath the mat and glued onto the step as well. These will trammel the mat very effectively, yet enable removal for cleaning beneath or washing.

Cast Brass Pads

These were in profuse supply some decades ago, but now seem to be impossible to find. They completely protect the step, and with their heavily textured surface, the stepper as well. Where they are now, nobody knows.

Silicone Non-skid

The fine grained silicone used in conjunction with paint for deck non-skids, can also be used in varnish with fine success. Simply tape off the area to be varnished or, if you're creative, make a stencil out of cardboard, cutting out either the boat's name or something useful, like "No Smoking." Lay in a coat of varnish, then sprinkle thoroughly and evenly with the silicone particles. When the varnish has set, vacuum or brush off the un-adhered surplus, and add another coat of varnish.

Meat Mallet Special

The owner of the vessel that had some of these pads in service wished to remain anonymous. Read on and you'll know why. Cut light gauge brass or copper sheeting the size you need, then place it on a medium dense towel over a piece of plywood or cement. Take a good metal-studded meat mallet and place it over the sheet metal, studs down, then whack it with a hammer. This will create neat little protrusions that will act as ideal non-skid. Move the mallet to the next area and whack again.

Well. Any grown man who'd do this would skip naked down Fifth Avenue at midday, singing fullthroatedly "Daisy, Daisy give me your answer true."

NON-SKID RUNGS

WINE CABINET

A finely fitted yacht must have a few bottles of white Burgundy aboard to wash down the poached salmon and moules marinière. Even though I had considered myself well versed in the ways of the world, it was pointed out to me by a dear friend that stowing wine aboard wrapped in sweater sleeves and sweatsocks did not really constitute the ultimate in elegance. Since then, we have installed a sort of a piece of plywood with holes in it into one of our lockers, but it comes nowhere close to the first class wine cabinet built into Grand Banks motor yachts (see illustration).

The entire unit is mobile, being equipped with four casters, so maximum access is gained to even the deepest part of the rack with minimum effort. The most limiting factor is, of course, size, for not only does the unit occupy 18″ of athwartships space in its "out" position, but it demands a similar run of flat cabin-sole inside the cabinet as well. The dimensions can be reduced, however, to about one-quarter the volume by removing the upper level and halving the depth of the rack. With a little shrewd spacing of the holes, one could still end up stowing six wine bottles in comfort.

So, first determine the absolute amount of space you can afford, then cut the hole in the cabinet face with a jigsaw. Next, cut the outboard piece (back) from a piece of 1/2″ plywood, and make up the front piece to the same dimensions out of four 3½″ wide pieces of 13/16″ stock patterned into a frame. Use either lap joints or dowels to secure the corners (see "Tool" section for doweling). Fill the area between the frames with teak plywood, cane, or louvers. Next, measure the absolute depth of the cabinet, including the front and back pieces. You will need to know this to make the fit as tight as possible so all play and movement can be avoided. Cut two shelves from 1/2″ ply to the depth of your space, minus 1 5/16″, and a width that's 1/2″ less than the width of your front piece. You'll need that 1/2″ space to trim each side of the plywood shelves with 1/4″ teak strips. Next, get your most favourite bottles of wine and liqueurs and lay them out over your shelves in the most economical way possible. A 3/4″ space between bottles is quite sufficient. Cut out the holes with the appropriate hole saws, or, if those are unavailable, use a jigsaw. To expedite matters, clamp the two shelves together and cut at once. Lightly sand all the holes to remove splinters. From 1/4″ plywood, cut a piece identical to the shelves, and glue it and clamp it to the bottom of the lower shelf. This is to keep the bottles from falling through and dragging on the cabin sole.

THE FINELY FITTED YACHT

WINE CABINET

You will now have to purchase a set of four casters. To do without them and just use wood slides would result in too much friction with such a substantial weight as six bottles. Once you've bought your casters, you will be able to determine how high you can install your lower shelf. Leave at least 1/4" clearance between the face of the cabinet and the cabin sole. A 4" space between the upper and lower shelves will be enough. Use cleat stock per diagram and #10 P.H.S.M. screws. Do not drill or screw through the face of the front piece. Now, decide how far you want the cabinet to roll out, and run a piece of cleat stock across its path to act as a stop against the back wheels. Lift the rear wheels over the stop and slide the cabinet into place.

With such weight and mobility, a very positive lock system should be devised to keep the cabinet in check. The use of three, high quality, barrel bolts would be advisable, one on top and one in each side. The top one is, of course, the safety that will naturally "fall" in any vibration and keep the cabinet closed.

If, at some point, you develop a taste for a new wine whose bottle fits too loosely into the shelf holes; don't panic; just slip it in a sweat sock and put it back in place; which puts us aesthetically back to where we were before we started building this edifice to bloodshot eyes.

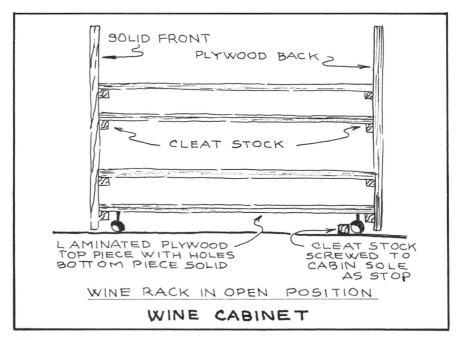

SOLID FRONT

PLYWOOD BACK

CLEAT STOCK

LAMINATED PLYWOOD
TOP PIECE WITH HOLES
BOTTOM PIECE SOLID

CLEAT STOCK
SCREWED TO
CABIN SOLE
AS STOP

WINE RACK IN OPEN POSITION

WINE CABINET

PIPE BERTHS

Once upon a time, before the major goal of yacht designers was to try to fit 67 berths into a 30′ boat, extremely pleasant wooden yachts were built with two comfortable settee berths in the salon and sail storage in the forepeak. This was a very sensible and suitable arrangement for couples but left a lack on those occasions when guests were to spend the night aboard.

Pipe berths became popular at that time, and some beautifully made ones, like those found on the graceful cutter "Nan of Clynder" from Greenock, Scotland, should deserve consideration on any modern yacht. Instead of having the salon inundated with bunks until it looks like a boy scout hut, pipe berths can be fitted over·each settee to serve as cleverly disguised settee backs during the day, and when hinged up, comfortable quarterberths by night.

Although various combinations of materials can be used, ranging from wooden boxes with bedspring bottoms to handsome bent aluminum tubing with slip-on covers, the most serviceable ones, from the standpoint of both construction and appearance, seem to be the galvanized pipe berths with a stretched and laced dacron base and an upholstered, slip-on foam mattress.

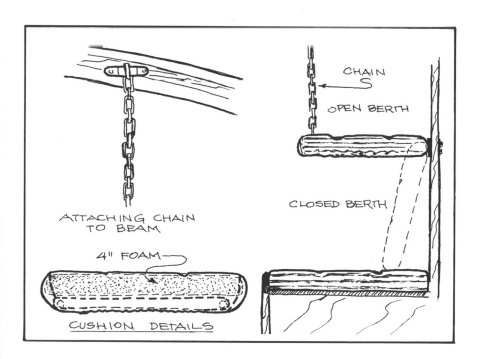

ATTACHING CHAIN TO BEAM

4″ FOAM

CUSHION DETAILS

CHAIN

OPEN BERTH

CLOSED BERTH

Standard 3/4" galvanized pipe is very inexpensive and if the berth measurements are accurately taken, any plumbing shop will cut the pipe to the required lengths and treat them appropriately. Be sure to tell them that the pipes will be assembled into a closed rectangle so they can cut you an elbow with reverse thread to enable you to assemble the last piece suitably. When measuring for the pipe berth, leave a 1/2" space between the ends of the berth and the bulkheads for ease of maneuvering. The gap can be largely covered up when fabricating the upholstery. The width of the berth will be determined by the current height of the settee's back, but a good guideline would be 20" for cold climates and 24" for hot ones.

Assemble three sets of brackets as shown and bolt them onto the back of the settee. To keep the pipe berth from sliding fore or aft, drill two 1/8" holes in the pipe directly fore and aft of the bracket at the foot of the berth, tap the holes, and screw a 1/8" machine bolt into each. The heads of the bolts will act as stoppers.

Next, use a piece of discarded sailcloth to form the bottom of the berth. Good dacron will stretch and sag much less than canvas or any other material. Allow for fold-under flaps of at least 4". For extra strength where the grommets are to be installed, run a piece of heavy dacron tape and triple fold the hem. The lacing should be set up as shown. A 3" or 4" thick foam cushion should be cut to the exact length and width of the berth and upholstered as described in the "Cushions" section with one exception. Run the fabric an extra four inches to form a flap under the berth, sew a tubing into it, and fit it with a draw cord. This will enable you to readily remove the cushion for cleaning etc. You will of course have to leave cutouts for the hinges in much the same way as you did for the dacron base. Leave gaps on the inboard edge for two chain supports as well, but make the cushion full in the corners. To support the berth in "back-rest" position, screw a block on each bulkhead to hold the berth in the angle desired. A 15° slope is quite comfortable.

To support the inboard edges of the pipe berth in the "up" position, bolt two padeyes through two deck beams about 18" from the foot and the head of the berth, then secure a length of 3/16" chain to the head and foot of the berth respectively, then hook the ends into the padeyes. You may find it advantageous to leave a bit of extra chain so slight adjustments can be made to the plane of the berth on prolonged and excessive heels.

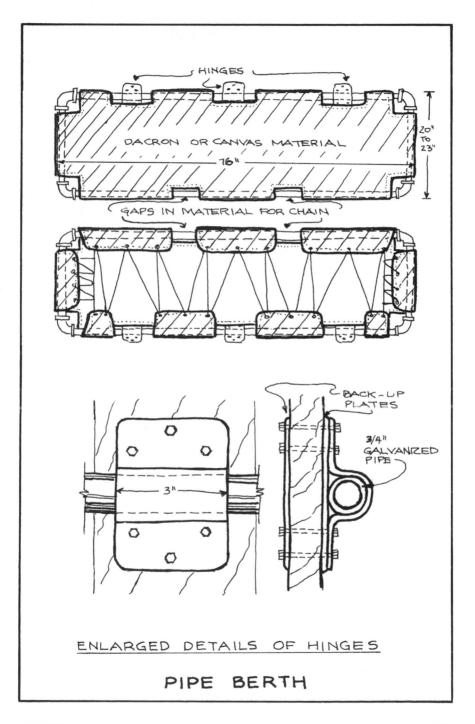

HINGES

DACRON OR CANVAS MATERIAL

76"

20" TO 23"

GAPS IN MATERIAL FOR CHAIN

BACK-UP PLATES

3/4" GALVANIZED PIPE

3"

ENLARGED DETAILS OF HINGES

PIPE BERTH

CUT FLOWERS ABOARD

Few things add as much simple beauty to a well-equipped cruising yacht than some freshly picked flowers collected on the most recent jaunt ashore. If kept aboard, they will bring back fine memories for some days after the port has long been left behind. The problem, of course, is where do you find a vase that won't tip over during the first heel. The answer has been discovered by Susan Hiscock who found a beautiful little half-vase during their cruise in the Greek Islands. A half-vase is a creature that has been cut in half lengthwise and thus, has a flat back, usually fitted with a hole through which it can be secured to a bulkhead. Because it is so high, with a bulbous lower half, almost no water will spill, if one cleverly fills the bulbous part only half full. This principle will only work if the vase is mounted on an athwartships bulkhead, otherwise, spillage will quickly occur along the flat side.

The second alternative is to have a long container held in a gimballed bracket similar to ones that hold kerosene bulkhead lamps (see "Gimballed Plant Holder"). Any ceramic container that fits in the bracket should suffice, although special attention should be given to having the vase's bottom weighed down (a few large pebbles should do) to encourage gimballing. The vase should not be filled higher than the bracket.

The third and most permanent way to display your favourite flowers would be to press them (in a book), dry them, and mount them under glass in small picture frames. These will enhance almost any bulkhead.

The processes of preservation are many. Some people advocate spraying the flowers very lightly with varnish, while others simply mount them on paper and frame them. Whichever way you select, they will rekindle beautiful memories for a long time.

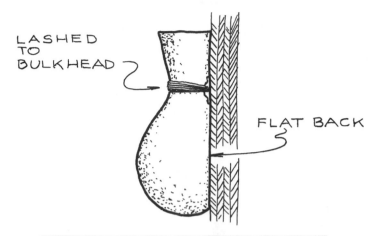

LASHED
TO
BULKHEAD

FLAT BACK

CUT FLOWERS ABOARD

FOLD-UP TABLE/MAGAZINE RACK

Most multi-functional inventions frighten me. As a matter of fact, I have developed such an aversion to them that I now refuse to wear a reversible jacket; but this combination flip-up table and magazine rack I find captivating. It would serve very well in narrow walkways plus have the advantage over a regular flip-up table in that it functions as a magazine holder in its "down" position. A removable crossbar holds the magazines in place. A hinged butterfly support holds the table in the "up" position.

H. & L. Marine sells a very handsome ready-made version, but if you want to build your own, here's how.

From 13/16″ teak or mahogany stock, cut one 2½″ × 16″ piece, and two 3½″ × 13″ pieces. Shape one side of the two short pieces as in the diagram, leaving a 1/2″ high by 4″ long bulge in its center. Route a 1/2″ × 1½″ hole about 1/2″ back from the edge. These holes will house the crossbar for the magazines. Bullnose all long edges of these two pieces. Next, 5/8″ in from the edge of all three pieces, dado a 3/8″ × 3/8″ groove running the full length of the 16″ piece and terminating within 3/8″ of one end of the two 13″ pieces. If you forget to terminate there, you'll have two bizarre little holes showing in your table front. Now square out the end of these grooves with a 3/8″ chisel and cut a piece of 3/8″ mahogany plywood to a 12½″ × 16¾″ shape, glue mercilessly, and slip it into your grooves. Reinforce the whole thing by side screwing (countersunk of course) the two sides of the table to the front piece, and by running a couple of screws (#8 by 3/4″ is plenty) through the sides directly into the plywood. Plug and trim.

The last remaining step is the butterfly support. The butterfly is much to be preferred in these situations because it allows the horizontal piano hinge to run almost equal amounts on both sides of the support. To achieve an ideal fit, both the fixed and the mobile parts should be cut from a single paddle-shaped piece of 1/2″ plywood whose overall height can be 10″ and width 14″. Cut the paddle into two pieces per the diagram and after cutting piano hinges to length with a hacksaw, install them before securing the fixed piece to the bulkhead with five or six 1″ P.H.S.M. screws.

FOLD-UP TABLE/MAGAZINE RACK

STEREOS AND SPEAKERS

There is something inexplicably emotional about being on a vessel that's moved only by the wind, but what's unavoidably tear evoking is having Bruch's *Scottish Fantasy* or Beethoven's *Pastorale* rising joyfully from belowdecks. Show me a man aboard with dry eyes and I'll show you a man with a dead hearing aid.

But beautiful music requires at least adequate equipment, otherwise you can bypass the whole thing and just hum old tunes. The most ideal system appears to be a stereo cassette. The quality exceeds that of eight-track, the machine itself is noticeably smaller, and the cassettes themselves have a more civilized appearance than the oaf sized eight-track tapes.

If undertaking lengthy cruises upon which new friends from different areas will be met, a cassette with recording abilities should be considered. It is truly a great joy to listen to forgotten voices. Another fine advantage of such a system is its ability to record from the AM and FM radio which usually accompanies it. Something like a Sanyo FP33M AM-FM cassette recorder, which retails at about $150, seems ideal. The speakers purchased should be the best car speakers available. Jensen's 9" ovals (about $60 a pair) with built-in tweeters have less distortion than most and put out a generally fine quality sound.

The awful plastic facing must be removed and tasteful speaker boxes should be built of teak and fabric. The Jensen speakers can be nicely accommodated in a space 12" wide, 7" high, and 6" deep. Try to pick shallow, hard to use corners in bookshelves, etc.

The sides (an existing bulkhead can make up one side) should be fitted to the curvature of the hull and underdeck from 3/4" teak, mahogany, etc. Cleat stock it in place. Place the vertical cleat stock 1" back from the front edge. This will serve as a mounting base for the face. Bring the wires through into the box with a good 15" to spare.

From 1/2" plywood, fabricate a face to fit snugly between the sides against the cleat stocks. Cut a hole sufficient for the speaker and mount same in the face. Cover the entire face with fabric that's left over from your cushions (not naugahyde), wrapping it clear around the back and affixing it there with brass or monel staples. Hook up your wires and slip the face in place. Attach it there with two brass round head screws. Use no glue. You never know when you need to get in there. Now slip in *Pastorale* and get out the hankies.

THE FINELY FITTED YACHT

STEREOS AND SPEAKERS

SLIDING DOUBLE BERTH

Most boat owners, myself included, demand a comfortable double berth on board. On large vessels, this need creates no problem to designer or builder, but on a vessel of 30 feet or less, the only solutions seem to be a forepeak with a V-filler or a converted dinette. Both have severe limitations. The former usually results in very cramped quarters caused by the low foredeck, and also gives birth to a cumbersome filler-cushion for which space must be found when not in use.

The latter is a major problem because its prerequisite is the existence of a dinette that, in most small boats, means extremely uncomfortable seats (the outboard edges of most dinettes are wedged beneath the side-decks which causes one's head to bend so far forward as to make any movement of the jaw impossible), as well as the destruction of an extremely valuable seaberth.

With this in mind, I propose that the illustrated sliding berth found on CT 37's is the work of a genius. It can convert a single berth in the main salon into an ample, airy double, while preserving the integrity of the single seaberth.

Most salon berths can be remodelled at a very moderate expense. The top of the existing berth can be left (if solid, i.e. non-sliding) and the new slats can be installed directly on it. If the current berth is sliding (i.e. a narrow settee converting into an acceptable single), just remove the original slides and, using the existing fore and aft foundation, install the new slides.

The slides will be fabricated from 1″ stock ripped to 4″ widths. To figure out the number of lineal feet you'll need, measure the width of the bulk (berth face to hull) at its middle to get the average width, then divide the bunk length by four and multiply the result by the average width, i.e. L/4 × average width.

Dado both sides of each piece removing one-half the thickness *plus* 1/16″ to a width of 3/8″. The extra space (1/8″ total) will allow for swelling. Lay the first board next to a bulkhead with dado down, tongue up. Allow this, as well as all other pieces, to overhang the berth face by at least 3″. Glue and screw inboard and out. Beside this, slip in the next piece with tongue down. Using a 1/16″ spacer on either side, put down the third piece (tongue down), and glue and screw it into place. Remember to use spacers on both sides of the loose piece *and* on both its inboard and outboard ends to keep everything parallel and avoid jamming. Repeat this procedure until you run out of bunk. At the end, your last piece will have to be

SLIDING DOUBLE BERTH

tongue up and screwed down firmly. If your order doesn't come out that way, throw out the last *loose* piece and make your *fixed* piece as wide as need be.

Next. Cut a piece of 2″ × 3″ to match the length of the berth, slip it wide-face up below the 3″ overhang of the slides, and screw and glue it to every *loose* piece with two countersunk 1½″ #10 P.H.S.M.S. per slide. Remember your spacers again, this time on the inboard end only. Now, trim off all ends flush to the inboard edge of the 2″ × 3″, and trim out with a piece of teak or mahogany as shown. Allow trim to form a searail 1½″ to 2″ above the slides to hold the cushions in place.

To support the berth when it's pulled out, you'll need two legs about 18″ from either end. These can be of either wood or metal. If you choose wood, make it 3″ wide with a 3″ wide hinge on its top so it can swing up and out of the way. Hold it up with a small barrel bolt.

If you choose metal, you'll have to find two receptacles per leg which will stabilize the leg as well as keep the cabin sole and berth from being worn through. In either case, a stop will be needed on the lower face of the slides, at least 4″ from their outboard ends. One length of 3/4″ cleat stock screwed from below with a single screw to each slide will do nicely. It will also help to rigidify the whole structure.

Your cushions will have to be the same thickness as the seat and of such a width that the seat plus the back will fill in the extended bunk.

Now cuddle up.

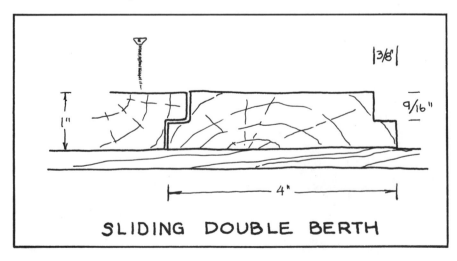

SLIDING DOUBLE BERTH

lamps/
stoves

WOOD AND COAL BIN

Any well-fitted yacht north and south of the 30th latitudes will probably have a little solid fuel heater, for those nasty winter nights when nothing can replace the comfort of flickering flames. Such a solacing companion as a wood burning stove deserves a special place for storing its food.

Even though these marvels barely nibble at the fuel compared to the amount of heat they produce, a two-cubic-foot storage space allotment would be a consummate notion. Unused vertical space is most ideal, like that next to the foot of a settee berth, or at the end of a fore and aft salon table. Of course, proximity to the stove is most desirable. Since possibilities for shapes and sizes are unlimited, I will humbly describe the one in *Warm Rain* as an example. We designated space for our bin at the junction of our centre table and the berth foot locker top. The space remaining allowed us to construct a bin $12'' \times 9'' \times 30''$ deep, yielding a volume of 1.8 cubic feet. We had a stainless steel, open-topped box welded to fit the space, and installed it with screws around the rim. The rim was caulked to keep dust from disappearing in the space between steel and plywood.

We had been told by many that a simple painted box would suffice, but we felt that a steel box would be the easiest thing to keep clean, and, in case of fire which could well occur in a place where bits of dry wood and paper are stored, control and containment could more easily be provided by steel. Of course, light gauge copper or brass sheeting would have been equally desirable, and as I recall, stainless was used either because of availability, or price, or a combination. For fuel, we frequent beaches for driftwood, or hardwood shops and boatyards for leftover scraps of oak and ash and maple. Hardwoods ignite less easily than softwoods, but burn longer. Of course, we have alder tidbits for the sweet smell of their smoke. In case of an emergency, machine pressed logs, chopped to thin slices, work very nicely; not too romantic, but quite warm.

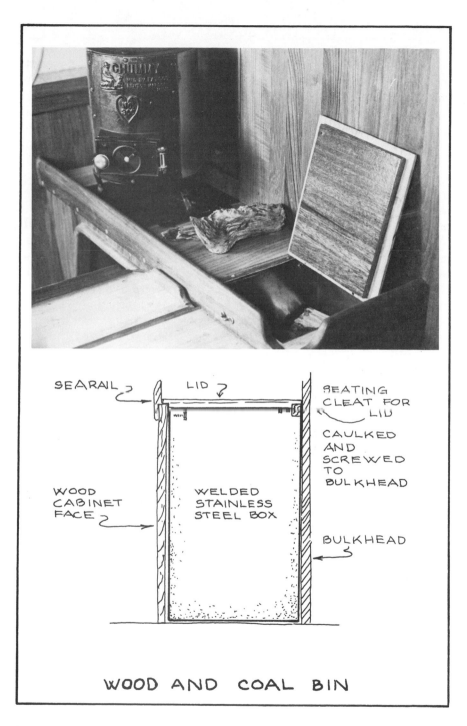

SEARAIL

LID

SEATING CLEAT FOR LID

CAULKED AND SCREWED TO BULKHEAD

WOOD CABINET FACE

WELDED STAINLESS STEEL BOX

BULKHEAD

WOOD AND COAL BIN

TRAWLER LAMP

One of the most beautiful and functional items that no yacht should be without is the Trawler Lamp. This is an all-brass, hanging, kerosene lamp with a white enamelled reflector hood and a circular wick whose circumference is over three inches. It is this combination of wick and reflector that creates a light strong enough to read by, yet one not nearly as cold and impersonal as the pressurized or mantel type lanterns.

Because of its large wick, the lamp throws enough heat to take the chill off most spring and autumn evenings; but because of this heat, caution must be taken when finding the lamp a permanent living space. If the cap of the lamp is closer than 8" to the overhead, a brass reflector plate will be required, otherwise the heat emanating in copious quantities all around the cap can scorch the wood. The diameter of this plate need be no more than 8"; shallow spacers (1/8") will be enough to create a dead airspace between it and the overhead.

Another small project required will be to tether the lamp when the vessel is underway since it tends to pendulate rather furiously. "S" linked brass chain is the most ideal material. Open the last links on each, then close them (with pliers) over the cap-supporting brass pillars. Next, install two small brass padeyes on bulkheads, salon table etc. so the chains will form a 35-45° angle. Now pull the chains tight and separate at the last usable link to the padeyes. Leave these last links partially open to facilitate removal when in port, for the chains tend to be bothersome during cross conversations.

Cleaning the glass chimney is vital at least once a week during constant nightly usage. Cleaning the white reflector should be effected periodically. The wick trimming is only an occasional task but it must be seen to. After many hours, the wick will lose its perfect horizontality, and small "high spots" will develop. These tend to burn with much greater intensity than the rest of the wick, and consequently, will be the first bits to smoke when the wick is turned too high (smoking should always be avoided to prevent flying, oily soot). To trim the wick, simply remove the globe, set the wick to the lowest setting where a bit still shows all around, then take a razor blade (tape over one edge so you don't amputate any fingers) and run it clear around, using the brass edge as a guide. Now light it up and let it roar.

THE FINELY FITTED YACHT

TRAWLER LAMP

MICA DOORS FOR WOOD-BURNING STOVES

All solid fuel burning stoves can become much more exciting if their flames can be seen from the cabin. Just opening the door is no real answer, for smoke and sparks can soon escape; but replacing a solid door, with one having a mica centre or a screen, would do the job safely and handsomely.

Since most stove doors are of the simplest type, with a gudgeon and pintle hinge arrangement, and have even simpler locking mechanisms, like a gravity-held tongue, replacing them with a mica door or screen is quite a pleasant and undemanding project.

Of the two, I would strongly recommend the mica door, since most tiny stoves are rather harshly affected by even the slightest change in their intake of air, to the point of turning into blast furnaces if uncontrolled quantities of oxygen are introduced.

The cast iron doors on most stoves are virtually impossible to modify, hence, a new door must be fabricated of brass. The simplest method involves cutting two sheets of medium gauge brass sheeting to the size of the door, leaving on a tongue as an integral part of one side, and two small leaves of sufficient length, to be slightly bent to act as parts of the new hinge. If the gauge of the metal is heavy enough, only the outside sheet needs to have this arrangement of appendages.

Cut out the central area of both sheets, leaving at least 3/4" of metal all around. To accomplish this, drill a hole with a 1/2" drill bit somewhere within the area to be removed, and inserting a jigsaw blade (hacksaw teeth) through it, proceed slowly to cut out the four corners. File all edges and corners as round and harmless as possible. Have a shop weld pieces of rod to complete your hinges, but be sure to have your whole door along as a pattern, so no mistakes in placement are made.

Gather seven of the tiniest machine bolts you can find, and drill holes (per diagram) to fit their shanks. Be sure your holes are drilled far enough in from the edge to allow for the nuts to fit on the inside, and not obstruct the shutting of the door. Cut your sheet of mica (sometimes it can be rescued from old irons) to fit well within the holes. Now you see why the 3/4" minimum perimeter was necessary. Slip the mica between the sheets of brass, insert the nuts and bolts, tighten, and fit the door into place. Now, just sit back and watch the beautiful firelight flicker on the bulkheads. My, oh my.

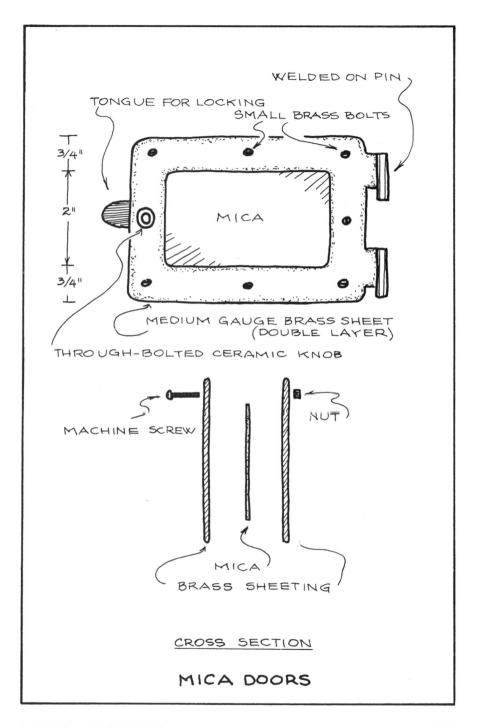

WELDED ON PIN

TONGUE FOR LOCKING

SMALL BRASS BOLTS

3/4"

2"

3/4"

MICA

MEDIUM GAUGE BRASS SHEET
(DOUBLE LAYER)

THROUGH-BOLTED CERAMIC KNOB

MACHINE SCREW

NUT

MICA

BRASS SHEETING

CROSS SECTION

MICA DOORS

LAMPS AND STOVES

LANTERN REFLECTORS

A reflector not only decorates and moonlights as a sometimes mirror, but it also makes a tremendous contribution toward keeping oil from sizzling, paint from bubbling and varnish from blistering on a precious bulkhead. It's one of those-to-be-cherished rare projects that one can actually finish in less than an hour, with most of one's self-esteem and hair untorn.

Very light gauge brass is an excellent and inexpensive material to use here, and although it doesn't have the reflective qualities of mirrored glass, it does look more shippy. For the average gimballed lamp, cut a $5'' \times 8''$ sheet with a pair of tin snips. Round all corners. Drill, or stamp with a sturdy nail, a hole in each corner and one in the middle of each side. Mount with brass tacks. For unlined glass sides, skip the holes, and after totally cleaning the fiberglass with acetone, epoxy the plate in place. There is no need to use the customary spacers between the plate and bulkhead. As long as the brass is well-polished and the lamp is the common non-pressurized variety, the added insulation gained from the spacers will not be required. Even if you are possessed enough to crank the lamp up to ridiculous luminosity, you need not worry about disfiguring your bulkhead; your coach roof will be ashes by then. Which brings us to the next point.

All kerosene lanterns should have either factory-made caps, or reflector plates above them. In the case of bulkhead lanterns, the factory-made mushroom caps will function infinitely better than cabin roof mounted plates. Because a gimballed lamp can, on a heel, actually lean as much as $45°$, an average lamp with an average chimney of $5''$ height, installed $12''$ from the ceiling, will require a ceiling mounted plate of nearly $20''$ diameter if it is to function adequately in such drastic situations.

At the same time, a $5''$ diameter mushroom cap extending out from the bulkhead on an arm, will cover the steepest heels, if placed no more than $2''$ or $3''$ above the glass chimney top. If you insist on using a home-made plate, calculate your range of deflections, and size your sheet of brass accordingly. This will, however, require spacers, for the heat from the wick will be coming directly at the ceiling, and it can be quite intense. The simplest spacers are those cut from $1/4''$ copper tubing to the desired length. Finishing washers can also be used. An $1/8''$ space between ceiling and plate should not be considered pathologically overcautious.

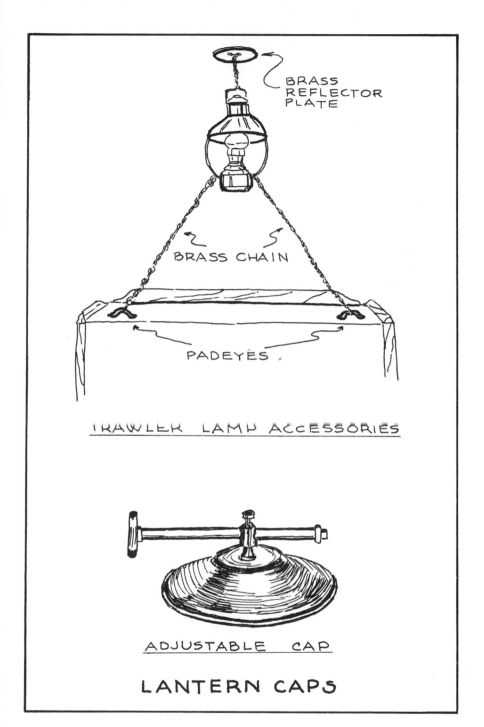

BRASS
REFLECTOR
PLATE

BRASS CHAIN

PADEYES

TRAWLER LAMP ACCESSORIES

ADJUSTABLE CAP

LANTERN CAPS

LAMPS AND STOVES 157

SMALL KEROSENE LANTERNS

Gimballed Lamps

For small areas, like the galley, chart table and forepeak where no room exists for the rather space consuming trawler lamp, the small and elegant two-way gimballed lamp can be used. The good ones have circular wicks and throw adequate light for most operations, excluding, of course, lengthy writing and reading. They hold about one-half pint of fuel, which even at full luminosity will last five long evenings. Installation of their caps and reflectors are mentioned elsewhere.

Anchor Lights

A well fitted yacht will most certainly carry a kerosene anchor light, if for no other reason than as a backup to the masthead or stern light. It can also act as a spare interior light or an efficient hand lantern for nightly deck inspection. I have often taken great joy in wandering on deck on a starry night, unhooking the glowing lantern from the gallows and taking a turn checking anchor line, halyards, or just ambling about searching for an excuse to linger and have the dark breeze ripple on my skin.

If gallows are unavailable, a brass ring lashed to the backstay will make a nice hanging place. Take care not to leave the main boom directly under the lantern for it may drip and damage sail covers and sails. The only special attention the lantern requires is during daytime storage. It should have a hanging place belowdecks with a short chain attached to its base to keep it from swinging wildly about. If placed on a shelf or the like, it may leak on a drastic keel. The simplest solution is to stick it in the oven of the gimballed galley stove. Just remember it's there. No one likes overcooked anchor lights.

LAMPS AND STOVES

KEROSENE FILLER RIG

On most yachts, refilling kerosene lamps and the small pressure tank for the kerosene stove is a major operation at best, a kerosene bath at worst. The kerosene, usually stored in a five-gallon jug, is impossible to handle with any delicateness (of which great amounts are required) when filling a half-pint lantern.

A sensible storage system and a simple apparatus for redistribution must be fabricated. A small stainless tank of say five to ten gallons can be custom made for about $60. It should be designed to fit some otherwise unused space, preferably directly under the deck, so a deck fill can be installed for major fill-ups. Try to locate the fill directly above the tank intake hole so an ordinary graduated dip stick can be used to check the fuel level; otherwise, it's virtually impossible to keep track of fuel used when an assorted number of lamps and a stove are involved. If possible, the tank should be mounted high to facilitate gravity feeding, and its outlet should be fitted with a 90° petcock. A copper tube should be run into the galley area and terminated in an accessible space (ours is below the galley sink). Affix an aviation grade flexible fuel line to the galley end of the tubing and affix another petcock on the end of this with a hose clamp. The length of the flex hose should be dictated by two factors: a) it must reach the stove's pressure tank, and b) it must reach the galley sink where the filling of kerosene lamps should take place. A word of caution here. When refilling lamps, spillage will often occur. The spilled kerosene must not be allowed to float on top of the water next to rubber or neoprene drainhose walls. Always have a bottle of liquid detergent handy, and when the first spill comes, squirt in copious quantities to neutralize the kerosene.

Back to the filler hose. The petcock on the filler hose must be safely stowed or it will open and spill the goods. We have managed ours without incident for three years by coiling our flex hose into a tidy loop and hanging it up high — in the narrow space between the sink and the cabinet wall — by means of a leather loop and cup hook. See "Rope Locker" for detail. We have also taken the added precaution of having the petcock on the tank itself accessible directly from the galley, by means of a hole-door (see "Through Bulkhead Access"), so we can be double sure of preventing a major kerosene catastrophe.

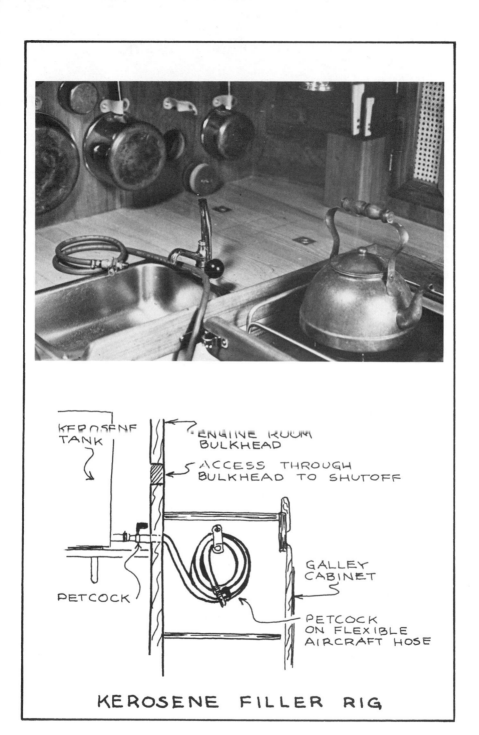

KEROSENE FILLER RIG

KEROSENE TANK PRESSURIZING RIG

If one's personal repertoire lacks having experienced total frustration, the immediate remedy is to attempt pressurizing the tank of a kerosene stove with that little insult of a pump that most manufacturers provide; somewhat akin to building the pyramid of Cheops out of ice cubes in July.

Step one to a better life is to heave the thing overboard. I normally abhor all pollution, but no one should be deprived of the inimitable pleasure brought about by the splash of this venomous little bastard. Do not throw away the threaded fitting that held the original pump in place. Keep the rubber gasket too. Next, purchase a small, good quality, bicycle pump, and buy a couple of spare rubber things that fit on the end. Now, scrounge up an old bicycle tube and remove the nipple intact, or better still, live it up and get two. Solder each of the nipples into a circular piece of tin, the diameter of which is determined by the opening of your tank. Reassemble the unit with the rubber gasket between the tank and the tin disk. The only task you'll have is screwing the bicycle pump fitting onto the tank each time and pumping a few strokes. Do remove the pump after using the stove and release the pressure. Not only will this prevent leaks caused by someone accidentally turning on the control knobs, but it will also help to keep fuel from building up in the manifold which will cause poorly combusting burners, smoke and big naughty flames.

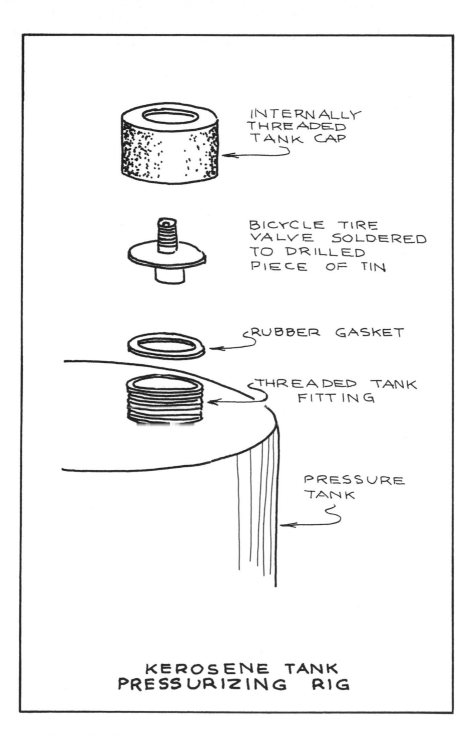

INTERNALLY THREADED TANK CAP

BICYCLE TIRE VALVE SOLDERED TO DRILLED PIECE OF TIN

RUBBER GASKET

THREADED TANK FITTING

PRESSURE TANK

KEROSENE TANK PRESSURIZING RIG

SOLID FUEL STOVES

Every cruising yacht should have a small salon stove of the wood burning variety to keep the cabin free of dampness, quickly dry wet foul weather gear, and, most importantly, to add an undeniably romantic aura belowdecks. Few things are as lovely on a cool night as listening to the rain patter on the decks, and watching the flames of a little wood fire.

Scraps of driftwood can be found almost anywhere and, with the aid of a sharp hatchet, they can be trimmed down to size with little effort. Most of the small wood burners are of a very old design, having comforted fishermen and tugboaters for decades, so their engineering has reached a very high efficiency, to the point where two handfuls (not armfuls) of almost any wood will keep a small yacht warm through all but the coolest of evenings.

The two basic kinds of wood-burning stoves are the bulkhead mounted, and the sole, or flat-surface mounted ones. Most of the modern ones, made of medium gauge tin or stainless steel, are of the bulkhead mount type. The more traditional ones, usually of cast iron, are generally sole mounted. *Warm Rain's* stove, aptly named "Chummy", is of the latter variety, and is affixed to a shelf with a bolt through each of its legs.

The stoves of either kind seldom take up more space than 16″ × 10″ × 10″, so lack of room is no excuse for their exclusion. The one important factor when selecting a stove, is the size of its top area. I feel that all stoves should be able to heat up a pot of tea or warm a dinner if the need arises. The traditional place for stoves is in the salon adjoining the main bulkhead. They should be located at least 18″ off the centreline to avoid smoking the sails, sail covers and halyards. "Chummy" is rather far outboard, so its stack comes through too close to the coachroof's edge, and has, on occasion, snared a staysail sheet or two. Halfway between the mast and coachroof edge seems an ideal compromise.

No major alteration should be needed for the installation of a stove. It can be installed as close as two inches from a bulkhead, so long as a sufficiently vented reflector plate is mounted for protection. Similar caution should be exercised wherever the stove pipe passes near any wood surface. A metal plate below the stove will not only afford safety, but facilitate cleaning up the occasional spilled ash as well.

Definite and strict procedure must be followed, however, when the smokestack is being fitted through the coachroof. The keystone

SOLID FUEL STOVES

of this entire operation is the double-walled, air-cooled, through-deck fitting, a proven one of which must be purchased and installed. A complete representation of the necessary parts is given in the illustration. One should not rear in horror upon first glance, for everything shown is a very standard, and not prohibitively expensive, manufactured item made especially for marine use, hence, of all stainless steel or a corrosion resistant alloy. The most common size of stock and fittings is 3" diameter, and that's fine, because most marine stove fabricators know this, but if you purchase a stove with an unusual smoke outlet diameter, be prepared to have some time-consuming custom work done. If the above does occur, try to have an adapter piece made to fit directly onto the stove so that, after that single custom piece, you can return to buying standard parts.

The Charley Noble (chimney cap) is always a point of discussion and derision among yachtsmen, but general consensus has it that the round, flat cap gives very few problems in any wind, and on almost any point of sail. When things become rather extreme, one would be showing poor judgment by keeping the fire going and risking spillage of hot coals. We have used the flat cap on *Warm Rain* for the past three years and have received flawless service, even during a 40 knot gale.

The two key factors in having a properly functioning draft are to have as long a run on the smoke pipe as possible, with as few drastic turns as possible. The former can be attained by mounting the stove as low as practicable; directly on the sole is not a bad idea, except that potentially useful space above it must then be sacrificed. I have been aboard many yachts, ours included, where stoves have functioned perfectly with a straight stand of pipe of no more than 30" between stove top and coachroof. As for the turns, one should completely avoid all 90° ones, and substitute 45° ones in their place. This can be accomplished by resetting any of the store-bought 90° elbows. Just get one and start twisting, and you'll see what I mean.

Specific Installations

The heat reflector panels behind the stoves should be of 20-24 gauge brass or stainless. The shinier the plate, the more effective it will be. It should be large enough to overhang the stove by 2"-3" all around. If you dislike the idea of having asbestos and asbestos dust around as much as I do, then simply set the plate about 1/4" away from the bulkhead by means of spacers. The air circulating behind the plate provides a very reasonable alternative to the asbestos. A

CHARLEY NOBLE

 DECK FITTING

DECK

 NUT SPACERS

 FLANGE

 BUSHING

DAMPER

STOVEPIPE

 ELBOW PIPES

FITTINGS FOR STOVE

second very attractive but more patience consuming alternative is the use of ceramic tiles all around the stove. Describe the use to your tile store and ask for a demonstration on tile cutting; it will save you a whole pile of tiles. Lighter gauge brass sheeting can be used in areas where bending or forming will be required.

To install the through-deck fitting, assemble the stove, complete with as many pieces of the stack as the coachroof will allow, set the smoke pipes in their final position, and scribe a light pencil line on the coachroof around the pipe. Now remove the pipe, find the centre of the circle, drill a pilot hole right through, then follow with a hole saw. Cut only halfway from the inside, then cut the other half from the outside to avoid chipping the gelcoat or splintering the wood. Clean all dust out of the area, wipe with a damp cloth, then caulk generously with polysulfide, and install the through-deck fitting.

If you're planning to be in a warm climate where use of the stove would be infrequent, it may behoove you to invest in a threaded bronze deck fitting into which a flat plug, or the Charley Noble, can be screwed.

Now stoke up the fire and bring on the hot toddy and a good book.

STOVE ALCOHOL STOWAGE

It seems that the tiniest of inventions on a yacht often bring the greatest pleasure, and it is definitely so in the case of the alcohol stowage mount.

Like most kerosene cooking stoves, ours came with a little plastic bottle that holds the alcohol used in pre-heating the primus burners. The nasty little critter, of course, had no sealable top, and no matter where we stood it and wedged it, it got free, threw itself about, and spilled its precious contents, until all our food and clothing smelled like an old stairwell on Skid Row.

When Candace had enough of this, she took a piece of copper plumber's tape (a perforated copper strapping 3/4″ wide used to hold plumbing pipes in place), attached its ends to the side of a cabinet just behind the stove, about 2″ up from the shelf where the little bottle sits, and it now lives continually upright unspilling and very accessible.

Yet a better container exists than the plastic thing. It's a beautiful brass oiling can, which holds three times the volume and four times the glamour. Its flexible nozzle allows you to pump evenly, without the unavoidable spills so common with the plastic jug; spills that turn the stove top into a pyre.

Our gallon container of alcohol is kept in the lazerette, well away from anything flaming or even warm, and we keep a one pint container of it in the same cabinet as the pre-heating bottle, similarly kept captive by a length of plumber's tape.

All this mess can, of course, be avoided by the installation of a propane stove, but then a propane stove might just send you on an unscheduled sightseeing flight over the islands, *sans* airplane.

DIESEL STOVES

North of Norfolk or San Francisco, any live aboard yacht, or one used frequently in the winter months, should be equipped with a diesel heating *cum* cooking stove, or a diesel heater. Diesel stoves have been used by the fishermen of both coasts for over three decades, and are now engineered so that they will operate with a minimal output of soot. Indeed, if installation and maintenance instructions are carefully adhered to, the units will operate soot and trouble free, and what's most important, they'll do so at a heel of up to 40° on either tack.

Most of the galley stoves are not much bigger than an average kerosene or gas cooker, measuring around 24″ in width, 17″ in depth and 20″ in height.

Not only will they keep the cabin cozy day and night, and supply the yacht with wonderful quantities of hot water (through internal coils), but they will also cook and bake magical dinners.

In the summer, when the heat (emitted somewhat generally by the stove) would make belowdecks uncomfortable, a single burner Primus could be substituted, while the flat smooth stove surface is used as counter space.

The foremost manufacturer of diesel stoves is Dickinson Marine of Vancouver and Seattle. They furnished me with the following installation procedures and general comments, many of them applicable to most diesel heaters and ranges.

General Description

Operation consists of fuel oil being metered through a metering safety control valve to a combustion chamber of stainless steel.

The burner is welded to a rigid crisscross framework of stainless steel, which in turn is surrounded by fire brick, an inner connected mesh of stainless, and grouted with furnace cement. The walls in most models are layered stainless with insulation sandwiched between.

Being directly heated by the burner, the aluminium alloy top is fast to warm and quick to cool. The oven damper provides for continuous circulation of heat within the range. Through its use and that of the metering valve, regulation of the desired oven temperature and cabin temperature is easily achieved.

The products of combustion along with the accumulated moisture are expelled to the outside atmosphere through the flue pipe and do not enter the vessels circulation system.

One of the best-drawing Charley Nobles.

Diesel galley stove with very intelligently designed guardrails. The small gimballed Primus stove beside the diesel is for summer use.

With proper installation, the heat created by the unit (allowing for heat loss up the flue pipe), is absorbed through radiation into the boat from the top, the oven or the inboard flue pipe.

In addition to the production of warm dry air, the range or heater is capable of supplying hot water through installation of stainless steel coils seated in the fire box.

The factory has made the coils "field installable" for the ranges. However, the ranges are limited to a maximum of two turns of coil due to space.

The heater operates in the same basic manner as the galley range.

Installation Instructions

1. *Locating Your Stove*

Special considerations for a power boat are not required because the heel and pitch associated with this type of vessel is not normally of a long enough duration to effect the flow of oil from the control valve to the burner.

Because sail boats inherently are on either a port or a starboard heel while underway, special care must be taken in locating your stove to insure continuous operation. Most models are designed to be located athwartships on sail boats. In this position fuel will continue to flow from the control valve to the burner at angles up to 40° (either port or starboard).

If the standard model is mounted in line with the keel, it will operate on one angle of heel but only up to 10° on the other; i.e., if mounted on the port side it would operate on a port heel but go out on a starboard heel after 10°.

To remedy the situation described, the standard model can be altered to operate "in line or parallel" to the keel. This is accomplished through the use of a kit which is designed to secure the metering valve at the proper height, parallel and perpendicular axes, on the left hand side of the range. This will extend approximately three to four inches. If space is a problem, the valve could protrude through the adjoining bulkhead into a locker or compartment. If the control valve is to be located in any other location, extreme care must be given to keep the float level (line on the side of the valve) 7/16″ higher than the bottom of the burner and all axes relative to the line of the burner must be in alignment.

With the above modification complete, the range will operate on angles of heel up to 40° on either port or starboard tack.

For sail boat operation on a gravity feed system, consideration must be given to the location of the tank and the outlets. The fuel

Stainless steel, diesel cabin heater with a large enough top surface for a single pot. Note fiddles around same. The nicely designed nook is finished off with stainless sheeting and ceramic tiles.

level at varying degrees of heel must not drop below the feed level of the metering valve, otherwise the supply will be cut off from the burner.

No unit should be installed where there is danger from combustion vapor, i.e. gasoline motors, propane equipment, etc., as such vapors can reach the flame in the fire box and cause an explosion.

Where necessary, combustion air can be ducted from the outside to the burner area.

2. *Preparation of Location Area*

To ensure a seamanlike installation, all combustable surfaces adjacent to the range should be covered with 1/8″-3/16″ asbestos board and light gauge metal — stainless steel or brass gives the most pleasing effect. The height of the covering should extend slightly above the stove's top. Temperatures radiating from the stove would not likely ignite these surfaces but could char them.

A metal pan should be placed under the valve. In the unlikely event of any oil overflow the drops will be caught in the pan.

3. *Fuel Supply*

A 5- to 15-gallon tank would be ample for most day and weekend sailors. For most vessels, consumption is from one to three gallons in a 24 hour period.

The preferred method of supplying fuel is from a tank located higher than the level of the valve.

If gravity tank is your choice, it should be positioned so that the bottom is at least 12″ higher then the control valve. It must be vented and a 3/8″ copper fuel line brought to the stove for connection to the control valve. A good quality fuel filter complete with a positive shut off valve should be fitted into the feed line adjacent to the unit.

If the vessel is "diesel" powered, a small 3 to 5-gallon day tank can be located as suggested above, and a supply line run from it to the main fuel tank. A small hand pump can be placed in the supply line to replenish fuel in the day tank. If possible a day tank should have a site glass to eliminate the operator from overfilling.

A third method is possible for diesel powered vessels, namely the use of a small electric pulse pump to supply fuel directly from the main tank to the control valve.

We have reservation about the last method for the following reasons:

1. A fuel pump is one more mechanical device which can break down.

2. If the pulse generated by the pump exceeds 4 PSI, there is a danger of overflowing the valve and the burner, although there are low pressure regulators available to limit this problem.

3. Pulse pumps operated from a battery source and are subject to the charge available.

4. Should the fuel supply line prove defective, i.e. a puncture, fuel will flow unchecked.

4. *Securing The Stove*

The stove should be set as level as practical and fastened to the floor of the recess with bolts.

5. *Connecting The Oil Line*

With the stove securely in place, the oil supply line can be run in and connected to the control valve. The air must be bled from the system at all joining fittings along the supply line enroute to the control valve.

Flare fittings do not require any further sealant if the line has been properly prepared.

Do not over-tighten fittings but do tighten snugly.

In no circumstances should the overflow be plugged. Under some operating conditions a few drops of oil may drop from the overflow outlet, i.e. in rough weather. Therefore, a small metal container should be placed under the hole to catch spills, or a line can be run into the bilge and a container placed there.

Do not run a return line from the overflow to an engine tank because under certain conditions the oil may surge back up the line and overflow the valve.

engine room

ENGINE ROOM INSULATION

Engines are beautiful to look at, but never to listen to A deafening beast can be made into a purring pussycat with a few hours of effort and a pocketful of money. The two most effective insulators are sheet-lead and sandwiched neoprene, both very costly. I have seen boats use pressed paper tiles of the variety used in recreation rooms, but these are extremely fragile and frighteningly flammable. They can be sprayed with a fire-proofing compound, but then, the expense mounts to where it almost equals that of lead or neoprene.

For the ease of handling the variety of surfaces it can be applied to, and mostly for its lightness, I have always been a fan of neoprene. The stuff used for sound insulation has a layer of fibrous compound sandwiched between the layers of neoprene. Cutting can be accomplished with razor-knives or handsaws, and adhesion can be achieved with the aid of either screws, or a variety of glues and tile adhesives.

If screws are to be used, they must be accompanied by the largest possible washers to prevent ripping through, especially in areas where the insulation will be "hanging," e.g., the undersides of decks and cockpits.

Insulation should not be limited to partitions only. Any surface in the engine room that can act as a sound reflector should be covered to make it into a sound absorber. If only partial insulation is contemplated, then at least the following surfaces should be dealt with: bulkheads, doors, ceilings (underdecks or cockpit soles) and the exposed hull.

The next, single, most effective area to be dealt with is the engine pan. This is usually either of fiberglass or of stainless sheet metal, but whichever it is, it acts as a perfect drum, multiplying every engine vibration and transmitting it to the hull and to the ears. A simple way to dampen this effect is to build a plywood filler under the low end of the pan, then pour in tested quantities of two part liquid urethane foam. I mention *tested* because the stuff expands with an unimaginable force that could potentially deform or break away your pan. So experiment with it in a can or box until you get the knack, then pour in sufficient amounts that, on expansion, completely fill the space between the pan and the hull. If the space below the pan was used to allow seepage to pass from the stuffing box to the bilge, simply cut a piece of 2″ PVC pipe in half lengthwise, and lay it, like a tunnel, under the pan *before* you begin pouring foam.

ENGINE ROOM INSULATION

ENGINE ROOM SEAT

I have always found fumbling about an engine room quite enjoyable, made painful only by the absence of a decent place to sit. Since *Warm Rain* is a double ender, and her engine room is well aft in her pinched stern, bracing oneself on the sloping hull is somewhat akin to pressing with your knees on the walls of a crevasse, hoping like hell you won't slip to the bottom. All this is complicated by the presence of the shaft and stuffing box, neither of which I want to test with my weight, so the only solution was to build a seat above them.

I cut a piece of 1/2" plywood to fit a certain point on both sides of the hull. A width of 12" was deemed quite enough. Next, with a bevel square, I determined the slope of the hull at the points where the plywood rested, set a table saw at that angle, and ripped two lengths of 2" × 2" fir, equal in length to the length of the angled sides of the seat. Both of these needed minor adjustments, which I performed by means of a table sander and eventually a file. I then marked the hull around each end of the seat, removed the paint from the fiberglass with paint remover, then rinsed the hull with acetone. The seat was then put back into place and its bottom edges were scribed onto the hull. The angled fir pieces were then placed just below these marks and bonded to the hull with single layers of mat and cloth. When the resin went off, the cleat stock was painted, the seat put in place, and the four centres for mounting holes, marked. The seat was removed and the holes drilled in it, then it was placed over the cleat stock again and a pencil was used to mark the holes onto the top of the cleats. Once again the seat came off, and the drill was furnished with a wrapping of masking tape 3/8" from its tip to be sure I would not drill too deep and end up with the ocean pouring through the hole. The 3/8" holes were drilled and the seat was attached to the cleats with the four 1" panhead screws. These were not countersunk or plugged, so the seat can be quickly pulled if the shaft or stuffing box has to be removed.

Some people suggest simply bonding the seat to the hull without use of the cleats. This, of course, would be totally inappropriate, for major demolition would then be required to perform even simplest replacement of the packing gland.

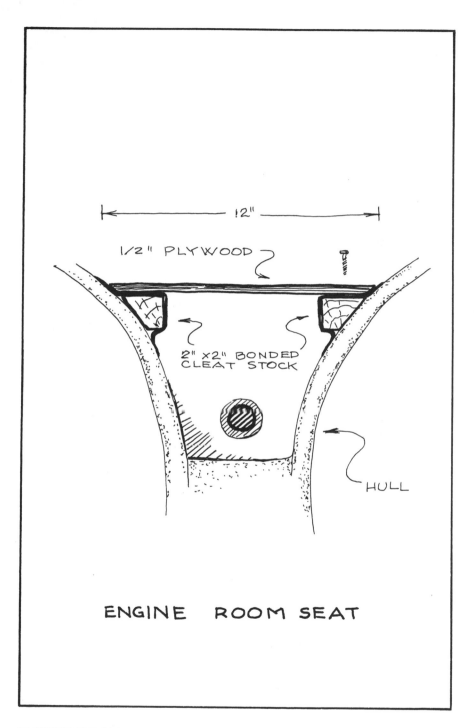

12"

1/2" PLYWOOD

2" X2" BONDED
CLEAT STOCK

HULL

ENGINE ROOM SEAT

ENGINE ROOM

ENGINE ROOM TOOL RACK

Perhaps some deem this a bit luxurious, but it's common knowledge that most engine rooms are extremely cramped, and once one is comfortably positioned, he will not want to leave to fetch a forgotten screwdriver. All engine rooms should have their own tools (this is the place most tools are used with greatest frequency anyway), and they should all be neatly and accessibly stowed in their own rack. Hours of searching and frustration will be saved in the long run.

I'm not advocating fabrication of shelves to accommodate a 150 piece Craftsman set. A careful study should be made of the most common tools needed and a rack constructed accordingly. As a general guide, I feel the following to be minimal: combination screwdriver, adjustable pliers, crescent wrench, magnet with flexible shaft, flashlight. Thought should be given to the tool kit most engine manufacturers include with their engine. They know which size wrenches, etc. are most frequently needed. If you have space, include them all. The minimal items above should fit handily onto a 5" high by 7" wide by 3½" rack, if arranged as shown in illustration. Since this rack will be going into the engine room, virtually any leftover 3/4" stock can be used. Cut out the 7" × 3½" piece first with radiused corners, then lay the pieces over each other in a vise so you can drill both sets of holes at once. I feel that the double rail system is necessary to avoid noise from rattling. If you're adamantly set against it, just do a single. I don't really mind.

Using your tools as templates, draw your cutouts and drill them. Attach the rails to a backing board of leftover stock. Glue and screw from behind. Now attach the whole thing to a convenient bulkhead, and just watch your next outing to the engine room become a pleasure.

ENGINE ROOM TOOL RACK

ENGINE OIL DAM

On some production fiberglass boats, I have been surprised to find no engine pan below the engine. In practice, that means that all fuel and oil drippings are free to proceed into the bilge to stink up the whole boat and mix with bilge water creating an awful mess. Belated installation of an engine pan is a mammoth task, but a considerably less demanding alternative exists. The bilge area directly foreward and aft of the engine can be dammed off so the oil will at least be confined.

There is no need to build monstrous edifices here, for the average small diesel seldom holds more than five quarts of oil, and in the event that all of that is somehow lost, your smallest worry will be cleaning up. So, fabricate two small dams or bulkheads from 1/2″ plywood and fit them into place. Next, take a 2″ diameter PVC tube and cut it in half lengthwise, sand the edges smooth, and set it below the engine so it just protrudes past each of your new bulkheads. Mark the bulkheads for the holes to let the tube penetrate, and cut to suit. The tube will become a sealed off tunnel, allowing seeping water from stuffing box, etc., to flow unimpeded to the bilge where it can be pumped out. Next, sand the convex side of the tube with as coarse a paper as you can find (a file would be better) to roughen up the surface, then clean off all the paint and dirt from the hull, and set the three pieces back in place. Using 6″ fiberglass tape cut in half lengthwise to make it more manageable, bond the bulkheads and the tube to the hull and each other, making sure you seal off every little crack to keep the oil in. Bond the bulkheads only on the sides that face the engine; remember, this is just a container, not a structural reinforcement. Be certain you smooth down all loose fibres while the resin is still wet, otherwise, they'll become savage little pins when hardened that will forever tear your skin when you're working below the engine. Finally, grab a little container of not too expensive enamel paint and slosh it generously over your new bulkheads to protect them from water.

Every few months, just dab up the oil drippings with a paper towel. It'll sure beat scouring out the whole bilge.

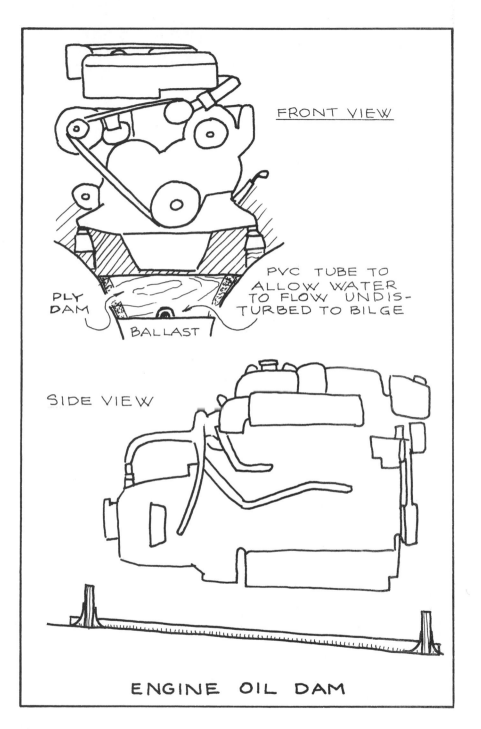

FRONT VIEW

PLY DAM

BALLAST

PVC TUBE TO ALLOW WATER TO FLOW UNDIS-TURBED TO BILGE

SIDE VIEW

ENGINE OIL DAM

SEA WATER FILTER

I think most people will agree that some sort of screen or filter system should be installed on all engine intakes to prevent the possibility of something big and ugly being sucked into the engine, causing blockage of cooling water and eventual overheating and seizing of water pump or main bearings. Admittedly, an on-hull-screen can be blocked by a plastic bag or other non-destructable matter thrown overboard by some mentally disorganized, but at least, one will have a single problem spot to investigate instead of having to tear down the engine bolt by nut. Some through-hull fittings have a screen cast into them as an integral part, obviating the need to insert extra screws in the hull. A regular bi-weekly check overboard just to make sure nothing has wedged in the screen would be a commendable idea.

A more costly and complex system, but one that allows instant inspection and cleaning from the engine room, involves the purchase of a salt water filter (see photo). This unit has four major advantages. One: it contains a cylindrical screen with a few hundred perforations through which the water is filtered after it circulates at a rapid speed around the cylinder. During this circulation, whatever has managed to find its way in through the seacock is violently rasped against the screen until it is eroded to "digestible" chunks, i.e. chunks that will fit through the screen and pass harmlessly through the water pump, et al. Two: the salt water filter is made up of a tempered glass cylinder so you will be able to tell at a glance if something is caught in it. Three: the large brass wing nut on top opens the entire top, making removal of blocked material very rapid. Before you loosen the wing nut, make sure your intake seacock is shut off so you won't flood the boat. Four: on boring afternoons in the doldrums, you can sit and watch seaweed and seaspiders and little fish swim around in the glass bowl.

Admittedly the system has another drawback besides cost in that it requires additional fittings in a water system, and of course fittings are usually the first to develop leaks. The potential danger of this can be minimized if thought is given to the location of the filter (just inside the engine room door would be ideal) so that inspection and adjustment can be done quickly and effortlessly. The wing nut, like most other brass fittings exposed to salt air or water, should be cleaned and oiled at least once a year. But don't forget to shut off the seacock first.

THE FINELY FITTED YACHT

ENGINE ROOM

THE ENGINE ROOM FIRE EXTINGUISHER

This fast to fabricate item could save many serious burns and many serious yachts. Fire extinguishers are, of course, mandatory in engine rooms and they serve very well as long as the fire is small, or discovered quickly, or both. If the fire has spread to any degree, access to the engine room may be impossible, and even if not, the opening of an engine room door may be all that's needed to turn the fire into a blaze by providing a fresh supply of oxygen. To cover the above possibilities, a fire extinguisher should be installed *just outside* the engine room bulkhead. Access to this extinguisher must be unimpeded. The installation involves no new equipment, except for a piece of copper pipe. Affix the extinguisher bracket to the bulkhead so that the nozzle points straight at the bulkhead into the engine room. Pay special care to have the trigger accessible without removing the extinguisher from the bracket.

Next, fit a piece of copper pipe over the nozzle and feed it into the engine room through a hole in the bulkhead. Have the pipe fit as tightly as possible. If you have to force the pipe through the hole with a mallet, so much the better. Have the pipe terminate just inside the bulkhead so the chemicals won't spray right over a part of the engine room. To seal the pipe-to-nozzle joint, slip the nozzle into the pipe as deep as it will go, then lay a bead of polysulfide along the seam.

Some yachtsmen have substituted rubber or plastic hoses for the copper. This is a grave mistake. In case of fire, the engine room end of the hose can melt, sealing perfectly the entire apparatus and rendering it totally useless.

A side note. If you feel the fire to be large enough to warrant use of this extinguisher, do not "crack open" the door just to check. Very bad facial burns have been suffered like that. First, pull the trigger and empty the extinguisher, *then* investigate.

An afterthought. It would show good seamanship to investigate different access apertures to engine room fires, e.g., vents, lazarettes, etc. just as a drill, so less time will be required during the fire for contemplation and discovery.

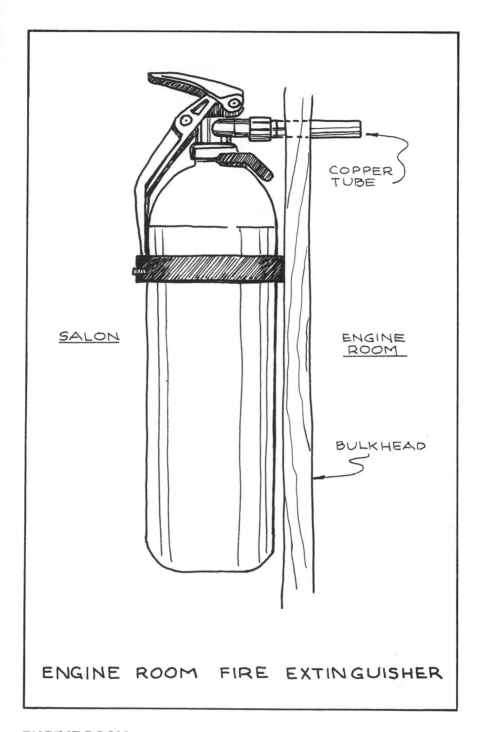

COPPER
TUBE

SALON

ENGINE
ROOM

BULKHEAD

ENGINE ROOM FIRE EXTINGUISHER

ANTISIPHON SYSTEM

In all vessels where the engine is located below the waterline, an antisiphon valve must be fitted into the cooling water intake line to prevent the engine from flooding. The valve is, of course, located above the waterline, and all it actually does, is break the flow of water by allowing air to get into the system; this causes the water in both hoses (up-to and down-from the valve) to drain off.

Even though most store-bought valves do work very well (especially the U-shaped bronze ones with float balls), I hesitate to use them in the engine room because even the best serviced and maintained valves seem to seep occasionally. This of course causes no problem in an area like the head, but in the engine room where vulnerable wiring and machinery is exposed, any amount of corrosive salt water should be considered a threat. The valve we installed with our Volvo diesel didn't actually seep, it actually sprayed, so after consultation with the naval architect and some engineers, a most satisfactory, foolproof system was arrived at that's one-tenth as expensive as the original and twice as useful. The conversion required no new hose, for fortunately, the old lengths worked well, so the only purchase made was a 1/2″ bronze through-hull vent (see diagram).

We discarded the antisiphon valve and mounted a vent in the cockpit directly above a drain. This position got the valve high enough to have it act effectively as a siphon breaker and its exposed location enabled the helmsman to glance at the valve occasionally to insure that cooling water was getting to the engine. On a normal yacht, that can only be determined by hanging over the side and looking for water coming through the exhaust, consequently, it's quite possible to run the engine dry for some time, unless, of course, someone keeps an eye on the temperature gauge which few people ever do. With the vent in the cockpit, a very steady trickle is emitted when the engine is running, a small enough quantity that it causes no deprivation to the engine, but large enough to be easily visible.

Some friends mounted the vent overboard. This has two disadvantages: a) it is not easily seen from the cockpit, and b) since it has to be mounted very high to be effective, usually near the sheer, the trickle of water it emits will stain the hull considerably. This stain, of course, occurs in the cockpit as well, but here it is shorter, less noticeable, and easier to clean.

THE FINELY FITTED YACHT

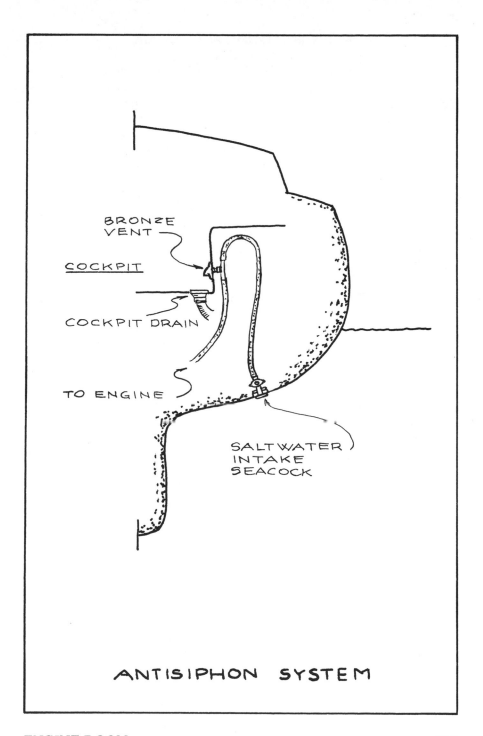

BRONZE
VENT

COCKPIT

COCKPIT DRAIN

TO ENGINE

SALTWATER
INTAKE
SEACOCK

ANTISIPHON SYSTEM

EXHAUST SIPHON PREVENTER

Many yachts have suffered engine failure and significant engine damage after following seas, entering through the engine exhaust through-hull, have set up a siphoning action that consequently flooded and seized up the engine.

I've been told that attempted looping of the exhaust hose and even installation of an antisiphon valve have proved futile, the former because the vessel's deck limits available height, and the latter because the corrosive fumes of the exhaust quickly rendered the valve immobile, thus inactive.

A recent idea incorporates the function of the highly looped hose and adds to it a safety precaution in the form of a hefty gate valve (see diagram). It is of course mandatory that the gate valve be readily accessible and it is most preferable that this access be gained from the cockpit where the helmsman on watch can shut it off as soon as he notes that sea conditions so warrant. On *Warm Rain*, the gate valve is mounted inside the lazarette at the very top of the lazarette bulkhead. Mounting is effected by two very large, all stainless hose clamps, which have first been completely opened, then drilled through the centre and screwed to the bulkhead. Before drilling and screwing you should do a dry run to determine at exactly what point the clamp must be drilled to have the clamp screw end up facing upward. If this bit of forward planning is done, both installation and later servicing will be made very much easier.

Care must be taken to run the hose well up out of harm's way, for I know of few other places inhabited by as dangerous a group of loose, nasty junk as a lazarette.

It would probably reflect excellent seamanship to have the valve closed at even the slightest danger of flooding. I'm told by the experts that one need not worry about forgetting to open it back up because the engine will simply not start if the exhaust is blocked. Be that as it may, we take the extra precaution of removing the key from the ignition everytime we close the valve, and slipping it into a little container inside the lazarette. This way we can never forget to open the valve when we reach for the key.

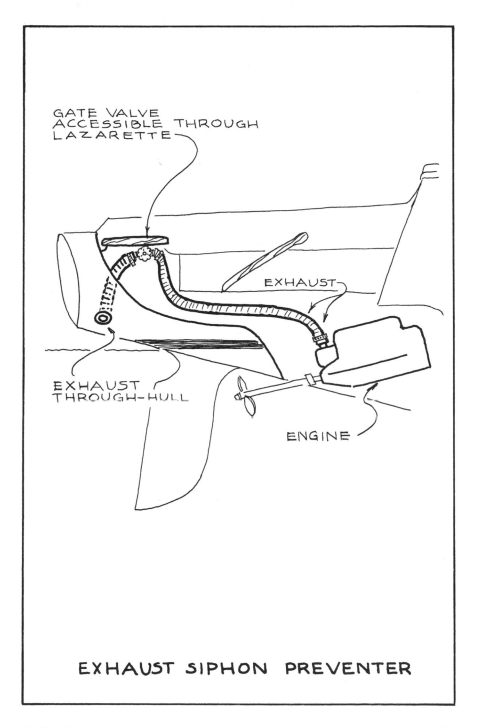

GATE VALVE
ACCESSIBLE THROUGH
LAZARETTE

EXHAUST

EXHAUST
THROUGH-HULL

ENGINE

EXHAUST SIPHON PREVENTER

ENGINE ROOM LIGHTING

I have always been shocked by people who regard their engine rooms as horrible black holes. We have managed aboard *Warm Rain* to bring in sufficient light, both natural and artificial, to make the engine room into a most pleasant place to work, or even just to sit around and lovingly fiddle with the old green diesel.

If the engine is located beneath the cockpit, the most practical and multifunctional source of light would be the installation of an opening portlight in the cockpit side that could house the ignition and other switches. (See "Portlight for Ignition.") If this is, for some reason, undesirable, then the most inexpensive method would be cutting a rectangular hole in the cockpit side and bolting a piece of 1/4" plexiglass over it. If the cockpit side is of unreinforced fiberglass, i.e. no balsa or plywood core, one should consider putting the plexiglass on the inside to prevent any potential knee scrapings. The bottom of the hole should be cut on a bevel to facilitate water drainage. All sides of the hole should be sanded round and re-gelcoated. The plexiglass should be cut large enough to overlap the hole by 1/2" all around. Bed it in silicone and secure it with round-headed bolts (head out) every three inches.

In wood, or wood-cored cockpits, the plexiglass should be placed on the outside to protect the end grain exposed by the cut. In this event, the outside edge of the plexiglass should be generously bullnosed.

The ultimate solution is of course to make the entire cockpit sole out of 3/4" plexiglass. This thickness is not sufficient to bear the load alone required of a cockpit, so strongbacks should be installed on the sole's underside (see diagram). To prevent the engine room from becoming a greenhouse, both sides of the plexiglass should be sanded with 100 grit paper to make it opaque. Because it will be sanded anyway, the plexiglass you purchase could be a salvaged or scratched piece. To make the surface non-slippery, 1/4" × 2" teak slats will have to be glued and screwed to it.

By far the most sensible electric light for engine room use is the fluorescent wand. This is a small plastic tube (unbreakable) with a handle and a spring coiled cord and it works on 12 or 24 volts. It throws generous quantities of light exactly where you want it, and if needed as a general source, it can be slipped onto a bracket mounted on a bulkhead.

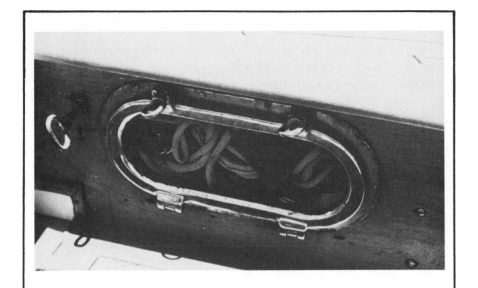

PORTLIGHT WITH PLEXIGLASS BOX
OVER ENGINE ROOM PROVIDES
LIGHT AND STOWAGE.

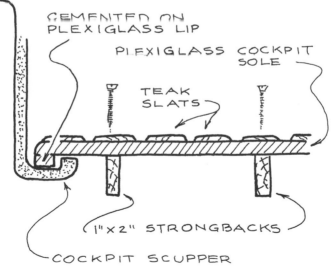

CEMENTED ON
PLEXIGLASS LIP

PLEXIGLASS COCKPIT
SOLE

TEAK
SLATS

1" x 2" STRONGBACKS

COCKPIT SCUPPER

ENGINE ROOM LIGHTING

ENGINE ROOM STOWAGE

Possibly nowhere in a vessel will one find as great a need for stowing obnoxiously-shaped objects as in the engine compartment. For the many odd pieces like spare alternator belts, oil sump pumps, and spare injectors, one will require nooks and crannies that are both secure and readily accessible. Both points are vital; first, because weighty flying objects can do horrendous damage to themselves and to delicate things like petcocks and glass filter settling bowls, the second, because lack of accessibility in choppy seas can lead to quick frustration and seasickness.

Tools should have their own special place, as should space demanding things like cans of spare oil, therefore, more will be said about them in following sections. For general stowage, the slat faced bins seem to be most practical. Through the slats, adequate vision can be gained of the bin's content and because of the slats, construction can be rapid. The bins should be narrow, about 8″, and moderately deep, about 12″, to allow most things to be wedged into place to prevent unscheduled flights. To help this wedging effect, the sides of the bin should be angled about negative 15°. If one end of the bin is a bulkhead, simply affix cleat stock at the mentioned 15° and make up the other end of a partial bulkhead of about 8″ average width, reaching from the lowest accessible point on the hull right to the underdecks. Fasten this new bulkhead to the underdeck with cleat stock and bond to the hull with fiberglass tape of mat and cloth. Bond on either side. On wood hulls you can screw, or clamp and glue, directly to a rib. This newly created vertical space can now be converted into bins with their plywood bottoms cleat stocked to each bulkhead and enclosed with 1/4″ solid stock slats cut to 1½″ width. All slats should be screwed to cleat stock or bulkhead, while the topmost slat should have a butt hinge at one end and a small barrel bolt at the other to affect a gate. The bins are now ready to house anything compatible.

One small point: spare engine parts are best left and stowed in their cardboard boxes. Not only will the boxes afford vital protection to delicate things like gaskets, but they'll provide a quick record of part names and numbers for the reordering and restocking which should be done as soon as possible after the part is used.

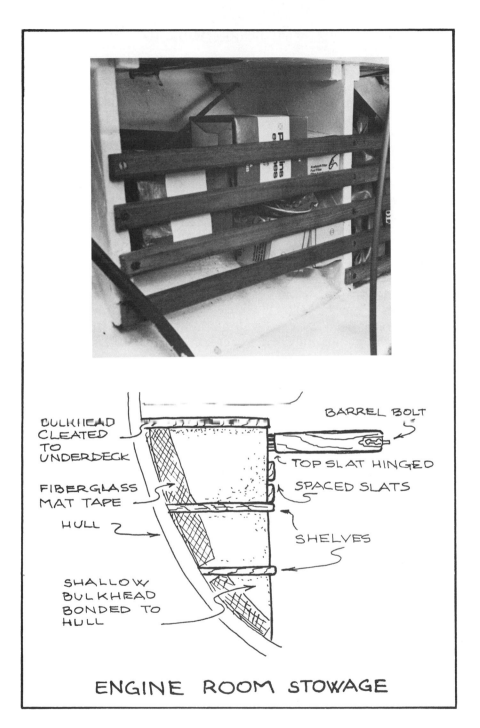

BARREL BOLT

BULKHEAD
CLEATED
TO
UNDERDECK

TOP SLAT HINGED

SPACED SLATS

FIBERGLASS
MAT TAPE

HULL

SHELVES

SHALLOW
BULKHEAD
BONDED TO
HULL

ENGINE ROOM STOWAGE

BILGE PUMPS BELOWDECKS

Without going into the history of lovely old pumps, let us acknowledge that in a well fitted yacht, a substantial manual bilge pump system is mandatory. An electric bilge pump is a nice convenience, although it tends to lull the crew into complacency regarding the surveillance of bilge levels which can often lead to discovery and repair of a leak. On the other hand, the electric pump is a useful warning system when the vessel is left unattended, alerting nearby yachtsmen with its constant buzzing if a major leak is present. Until the battery dies.

The ideal cockpit bilge pump is described in the following section. For belowdecks, a larger diaphragm pump like a Henderson or a Whale 25 would be ideal. The latter can move 25 gallons per minute quite successfully if thought has been given to its installation. Functioning in an emergency usually imposes great strain on a crew; so someone performing the doubly strenuous duty of working the pumps should be assisted by at least having: a) a comfortable place to brace himself, and b) copious quantities of fresh air to avoid seasickness. With this in mind, a location very near the companionway would be the most favourable, having the added advantage of quick communication with the cockpit. On *Warm Rain*, we installed a Whale 25 directly over the bilge, just under the bridge deck, at the entrance to the engine room. Being directly over the bilge eliminates the need for curves which increase friction and, consequently, the amount of effort required to move the water overboard. Being so close to the bilge also gives very rapid access to the strum boxes (strainers, see drawing) in case they plug up and require cleaning. Being at the entrance to the engine room, the pump man can act quickly when it's time for drastic measures like closing the engine intake seacock, cutting the hose just above it and sticking it into a strum box and into the bilge to gain the assistance of the engine salt water pump in saving the vessel. An average engine pump will discharge about 20 g.p.m. at 2000 engine rpm.

The pump should be mounted at a height where the least strain will be required in its operation. If the pump man is to be standing, the pump should be chest height. Clear access should be provided so that the pump man can pull the handle toward himself, then push it away on the return stroke, like rowing. In both cases, body weight can be applied instead of relying on sheer muscle power, which indeed would be the sad case, if the pump handle had to be worked by moving it from one side of the body to the other.

THE FINELY FITTED YACHT

Care must be taken at installation to leave sufficient space around the pump so it can be quickly torn down and cleaned should the need arise. To prepare for this eventuality, one would be well advised to tear the pump apart while lazing on deck on a sunny day with tools and manufacturer's diagrams handy. The pump should be torn down and cleaned and the bolts greased annually as standard maintenance.

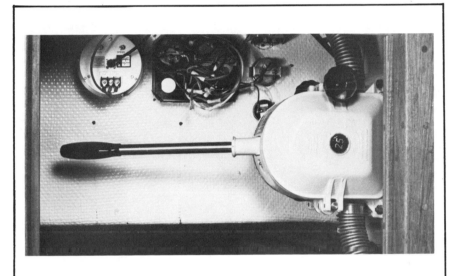

BILGE PUMP

stowage

STOWAGE GRATES

Almost any yacht will require a half dozen grates for sundry uses. Most of these will be rather small, necessitating only light construction and will be, therefore, relatively easy to make. Unlike larger grates in the cockpit or shower, which are called upon to support large weights, the stowage grates need only have one set of dadoed cross pieces. The uses for these grates will be many.

Ice Box

Since most good ice boxes are top loading, vast vertical space is normally wasted because no one likes to unpack the whole ice box to get at one little thing on the bottom. If the ice box liner doesn't have molded ridges to support shelves, seating cleats will have to be installed. Cleats 3/8" × 3/4" should be used on edge. All wood inside an ice box must be varnished or it will mildew. If room exists for a number of shelves, the upper shelves should be narrowest, with lower ones getting increasingly wider. At no time should any shelf take up more than two-thirds of the surface area, for access beneath it will be impossible, necessitating total unloading — which is what it's trying to prevent in the first place.

Against-Hull Stowage

No food or clothing should be placed directly against any uninsulated hull, or mildew will instantly attack it. This is true for fiberglass, aluminum, steel, and ferro cement because of condensation, and of wood because of seepage. The simplest way to keep air circulating beneath stowed items is to place light grates against the hull. These, too, must be completely spray varnished or painted to be mildewproof.

Construction

These light grates require 3/4" stock as wide as possible to minimize work. Out of a 36" × 6" board, enough grate stock can be cut to make a 36" × 12" grate, since one-half of all grates is air. Set a table saw with 3/4" dado blades at 3/8" depth, and run the board through widthwise, allowing 3/4" space between the dadoings. When a whole board has been dadoed, rip it into 3/4" strips. Next rip 3/4" stock to 3/8" thickness. Cut both the dadoed and 3/8" slats to required length and assemble using a 3/4" spacer between the dadoed stock. Glue with resorcinol and weight down. The sides can be trimmed with 1/2" trim, and attached with resorcinol glue and #6 screws. For ice box shelves, a searail of 2" height should be utilized to prevent playing the food version of Fifty-Two Pick-Up.

STOWAGE GRATES

THE DOLLAR FORTY-NINE ROPE LOCKER

There are few sadder sights than a dacron snake-pit. Anyone who stores hundreds of dollars worth of lines as if he'll never use them again, should be hung by them all at the same time. On the other hand, great pleasure can be derived from lifting the lid of your counter, reaching confidently into an accustomed spot, unhooking a leather strap, and coming out with the exact piece of line you were after. Now that's living. Some may argue.

Almost any spare lines (sheets, halyards, etc.) can be whipped into a modest coil and hung into a space no wider than 6″. Thus, a narrow locker 24″ × 8″ can house as many as eight staggered coils on its walls, and still have two hooks left over, one for the sail repair kit bag and the other for a small canvas bag housing odd lines. This little bag you will find your best friend, yielding long-forgotten treasures at the most dire moments, like when your belt buckle breaks.

The fastenings required are laughably simple, an even greater reason for installing them immediately. Leather straps 10″ × 1″ will be needed with an awl hole at either end to act as loops for the coils. These will be hooked to brass cup hooks. Only one end of the strap will be mobile when releasing or fastening the lines, the other can hang permanently on the hook.

If this isn't function in its simplest form, may Frank Lloyd Wright spit on my grave.

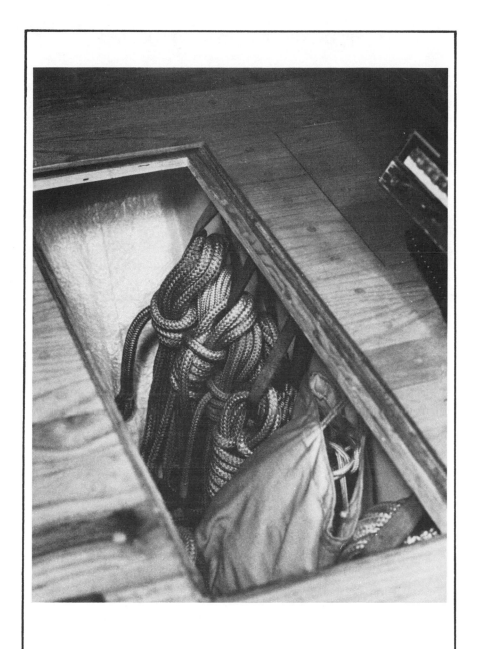

ROPE LOCKER

BAFFLES FOR DRAWERS AND LOCKERS

Most yacht lockers are rubbish heaps, those of our friends and acquaintances not included, of course. Due to their huge single spaces, they become bottomless pits for everything from shoes to onions, which then proceed to out-rot and out-smell each other for untold months, until a flood or a fire cleans them out.

Drawers

Any large flat drawer can easily be divided off into small civilized areas by using either 1/8″ wide plywood baffles or ready-made plastic trays. The latter have many advantages over the plywood and should be used in places where things may be spilled or leaked, like in the head and galley. Cleanup can then be effected by removing and rinsing one tray only, without the need to unpack the entire drawer. The plastic trays couple nicely together with molded grooves and tongues so they will not shift and slide about.

If you use plywood baffles, cut them 1/2″ lower than the sides of the drawer. Each piece should be let in half its height where it intersects with another piece. In plywood of 1/8″ thickness, any radial arm or table saw blade will be enough to cut the let in. Assemble without any glue or permanent cleats. If well measured and cut, the baffles will have enough tension to hold themselves in place and still be easily dismantled and removed for cleaning or modification.

Lockers

All lockers, whether top or front loading, that are used to stow drygoods, equipment, cans or vegetables, etc., should have a baffle every 12″ or 18″. These should, for the sake of flexibility, be readily removable. If little weight is involved, and ventilation is of prime concern (as it is with food such as dried fruits and vegetables), then baffles made of netting should be used. They can be attached by means of brass hooks that are screwed into the cabinetry, *not into* the hull. If the bottom of the netting needs to be secured, wedge and glue a piece of scrap fir or mahogany 2″ × 2″ along the bottom of the netting, attaching ends to cabinetry, and screwing the brass hooks into it.

If ventilation is of no major concern, as with canned goods, a 1/8″ plywood baffle, carefully cut to fit the hull curvature and cabinetry, will do nicely. There is no need to affix these to anything, for the force of the cans will be enough to keep them in place.

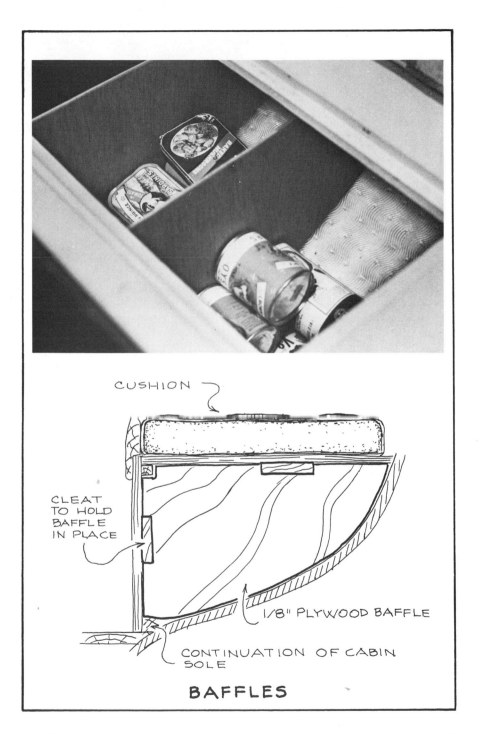

CUSHION

CLEAT
TO HOLD
BAFFLE
IN PLACE

1/8" PLYWOOD BAFFLE

CONTINUATION OF CABIN
SOLE

BAFFLES

STOWAGE   207

NETS

Nets are great: you can fish with them, slick your hair down with them, and catch butterflies with them. They are also one of the most important materials one can use for stowage, both exposed and concealed.

Exposed

We have found many uses for exposed netting on *Warm Rain*. These are the self-contained nets with hemmed edges and loops in the ends, for either hanging or carrying. We have one dangling from the dishrack, just above the icebox, for fruit. The fruit lasts much longer when not sitting against an unbreathing surface, the net doubles as a shopping bag, instead of the silly paper bags that rip, and it utilizes space that otherwise would be quite vacant.

In the forepeak, two larger ones are used — one, just below the foredeck where we stow our bedding during the day; the other, a smaller one similarly installed over the outboard uppermost part of the double bunk where it serves as a *necessaire* for late night goodies like books, flashlights, and teddy bears.

Finished nets are useful everywhere for endless knickknacks and most useful up high near the companionway for sailing gloves, strobe lights, suntan lotion, sunglasses, etc. On nice days, the net can be unhooked, taken out (contents and all), and hung conveniently from the gallows or lifelines, near the cockpit.

Concealed

In lockers, nets are a marvel. Finished nets can be filled with different fruits and vegetables and hung inside lockers, ventilating and out of the way. They are perfect for storing paper products, like napkins and paper towels, which usually take up great space and often become wet in locker bottoms.

Unfinished nets in lockers are also of great value and I saw a marvelous boat in Camden, Maine, whose name I cannot recall, using it most cleverly in all closed lockers, instead of solid plywood shelves. They greatly aid in venting, keeping clothes, towels, and shoes fresh.

The best netting to use is un-dyed cotton, for it's easily washable and it will not stain clothes. It can be purchased in bulk and cut to the required size; the loose strands can then be tied to a 1/4″ hemming line running clear around the net, with a loop at either end for handles. It can also be hemmed by sewing a ribbon of cotton around the perimeter, with an occasional 3/16″ grommet to be used for suspending.

COTTON HEM

GROMMETS & CUP HOOKS

NETS

STOWAGE IN COMPANIONWAY LADDER

Small compartments in accessible areas are at an absolute premium in most yachts and few better places meet both requirements as well as companionway ladders, into which small lockers can be built to house everything from flashlights and bilge pump handles to suntan lotion and sandwiches. Since most ladders hinge up to give access to spaces beyond, the overall weight has to be considered as well as the allowance of sufficient foot space for normal travel.

Willi de Roos' *Williwaw*, the first sailboat to sail through the ice of the Northwest Passage, has a ladder constructed somewhat pyramidically so the depth of the compartment increases toward the base. Between each rung is a hinged or sliding door, giving access to the compartments.

Since ladders vary in slope and depth, I shall describe here only the very simple adaption that could be applicable to most.

The one thing that cannot be tempered with on a ladder is the surface of the rungs. They need to be at least 5″ deep for good footing, hence, the storage to be added must be in the form of an upside down pyramid, with maximum stowage space gained just beneath each tread.

Step One involves sealing off the rear of the ladder. This can be accomplished by a single piece of 1/8″ plywood that is set into rabbets in the back of the ladder and glued and tacked onto the rungs and the sides. Next, install cleat stock angled from the back of the top of each rung to within an inch of the front of the bottom of the rung above. The face of the storage space can be of 1/4″ plywood split horizontally in a ratio of about two to three. To explain. The lower 8″ of a given face of 12″ will be fixed permanently to the cleat stock while the remaining 4″ will hinge *down* from two small butt hinges adjoining the two facial pieces. If you erroneously hinge the whole face, good luck. Every time you open it you'll be playing Fifty-Two Pick Up. Since most things stored here will be light, a single barrel bolt to one side will be sufficient. Space permitting, this would be an ideal location for a concealed paper towel rack (see Paper Towel Rack).

A word of logic, place the heaviest objects near the top rung and the lightest near the bottom rung. The ladder will be much easier to lift. Remember the wheel barrow.

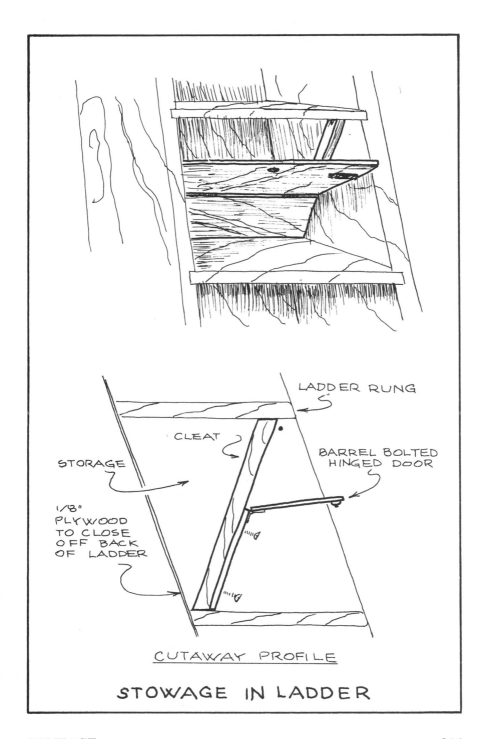

LADDER RUNG

CLEAT

STORAGE

BARREL BOLTED
HINGED DOOR

1/8"
PLYWOOD
TO CLOSE
OFF BACK
OF LADDER

CUTAWAY PROFILE

STOWAGE IN LADDER

LOCKER VENTING

Keeping all areas of a vessel well vented is mandatory, regardless of the material used for hull construction. In wooden hulls, dry rot starts beautifully in lockers and bilges where rain water has ventured; in metal hulls, the danger of rust is ever present; and, of course, rot can start in fiberglass yachts, whose plywood bulkheads are very vital, but very vulnerable, structural parts. Actually, the danger is considerably greater with fiberglass, since condensation is such a major problem, and if you think this is being nit-picky, just run your hand along the inside of your hull on a cold night after you've finished cooking a steamy dinner.

The first step in fending off dry rot, etc., is to provide each locker with a drain hole in its lowest part; this way, any stray water will drain off into the bilge before it has an opportunity to soak into any surrounding wood. The drain hole need be no more than 3/8". Periodic cleaning will be required to ensure flow. Sufficient ventilation can be provided to most lockers by substituting solid doors with louvered ones, or ones with cane inserts, or at least jigsawing out ventilating holes in a large attractive pattern, say in the shape of Dolly Parton's left boobie. For top loading lockers, whose lids are usually covered by cushions, holes can be cut in the locker faces, which can then, in turn, be filled with louvers, grates, or cane.

To facilitate inter-locker ventilation, drill three or so 1" diameter holes in the non-structural bulkheads between them. Drill these as high up as possible to be sure they won't get covered over by clothes or other objects. With all lockers thus interconnected, a further step can be taken to increase air flow. Lead a pipe from a dorade vent well forward into a locker in the bow, creating a sort of forced system which can flow through the locker and out through an aft vent. If the engine is aft, with its own vent, the lockers could be allowed to simply feed into the engine room and be extracted from there.

Use as many grates and vents as possible inside lockers, to facilitate air passage close to locker surfaces. If your anchor chain is fed below, through a piping system, into a locker which vents into the bilge, use of a dorade-shaped deck pipe, instead of the top closing flat kind, would be most prudent, for then at anchor, or on good days, the flap gate could be left open, creating a perfect air feed down through the bilges.

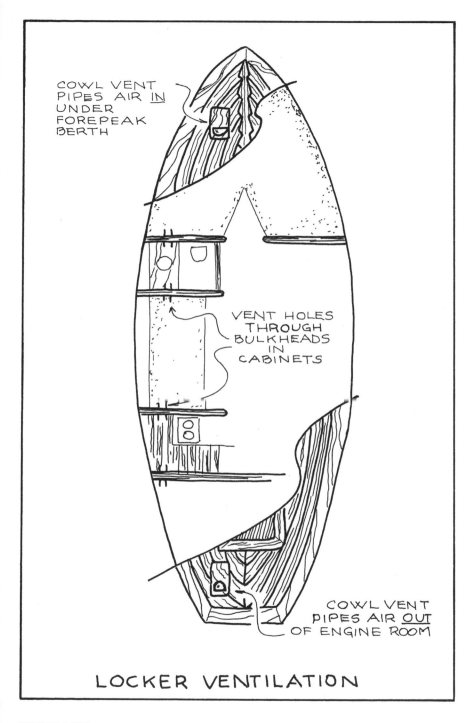

COWL VENT PIPES AIR IN UNDER FOREPEAK BERTH

VENT HOLES THROUGH BULKHEADS IN CABINETS

COWL VENT PIPES AIR OUT OF ENGINE ROOM

LOCKER VENTILATION

STOWAGE

FISH ROD RACKS

I don't like fishing. I don't mind dangling bits of nylon and chrome over the side, and I don't even mind paying for more chrome and nylon after some stupid fish makes off with the first set, but what I don't like is unhooking the slithering beast, bludgeoning it with my only hammer, carving flimsy bits of meat from its carcass, and ending up with two bits to eat and a cockpit full of guts to clean up. But those two bits are so good that I've buckled under and now regularly dangle, bludgeon, etc.

Of course, now there's a new problem: the stowage of fishing gear. Nothing is less entertaining than a hook in the seat of one's pants or other private places, so a most secure rack must be fabricated and used religiously.

Solid 3/4″ stock will be required in two 3″ × 12″ pieces for two rods. Add about 6″ more for each additional rod. The rack is made for collapsible rods, so for each rod, a large hole will be required for the handle, a small hole for the base of the tip and two small "J" ends. A 1½″ hole should suffice for the rod base, and about 3/4″ for the base of the extension. The "J"s should be routed to about a 3/8″ width. To save space, the second set of rods should be reversed, that is, the holes switched places with the "J"s. The ends of the "J"s should be equipped with locking tabs made of brass plate or hard plastic, secured loosely by a single screw or brass tack.

The mounting board of 1½″ width should be screwed and glued onto the edge of each rack. Mounting can be effected on either the overhead or bulkheads.

If you're to engage in activities such as cleaning and bludgeoning, you will require an official fish board. For the sake of stowage, this should be thin (1/2″ plywood is just fine), and about 18″ × 8″. All your cleaning and filleting can be done on this board. Drill a hole half way through in one end to accommodate a mounting spike, which you'll have to drive through the end of the skin when separating the fillet from same. A real hole at the other end with a lanyard through it would be a great idea to enable you to dangle the board over the side for a good salt water rinse. A scrub brush should be used to clean the board thoroughly after each use.

Botulism is no fun.

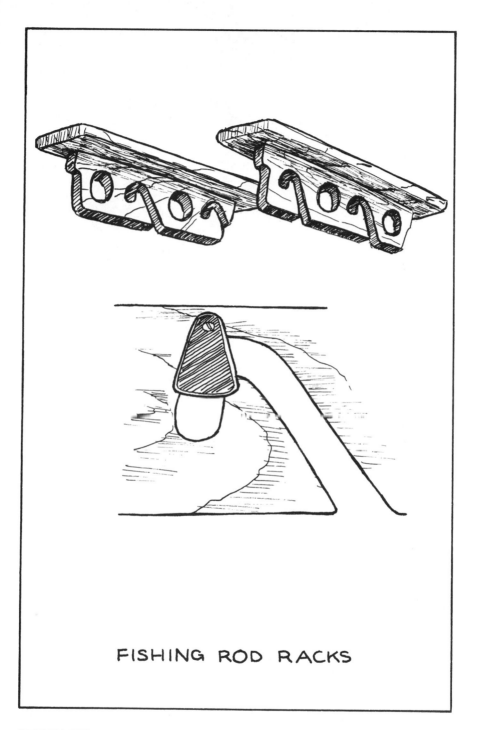

FISHING ROD RACKS

FOUL WEATHER GEAR DRYER

It's all ugly. Being wet and cold and having fingers like pale prunes, and lips like grape-sicles, and teeth that chatter nerve-wrackingly is all ugly, but it's even uglier when you have to sit in a cabin after all that with ugly dripping clothes dangling all over the place.

The best solution for both you and your soaked gear is to start a good roaring fire and hang the clothes in a well-ventilated place to dry, but preferably out of sight so they won't be constant reminders of your prunishness.

A major factor here is location of your heating stove. It's nice to have it on the bulkhead adjoining the head. Any further discussion will be based on the assumption that this is possible. Directly behind the stove, cut a hole about the size you had your reflector plate. On the head side of the bulkhead, cover the hole with fine brass meshing and staple it to the bulkhead with monel or brass staples. Trim the hole with "L" trim on the salon side and with a rabbeted frame on the head side.

The rabbeted frame should be constructed as follows: from 3/4″ stock, rip two 1½″ wide strips with lengths of twice the height of your hole. Also rip two smaller pieces whose length equals the width of the hole. Next, groove the centre of all pieces with a 1/2″ deep groove the width of your saw blade. Affix the two sides and the bottom onto the bulkhead like an open frame. Acquire a moderately gauged piece of copper or brass or stainless sheeting to fit the frame and cover the hole, and overhang it (downward) by 2½″. Attach a small porcelain handle to the bottom of the plate. Across the top of the hole, fit a 2″ strip of 1/4″ plywood, then affix it so that the plate will cover the entire piece when in a down position. Slip the plate in place and install the grooved top of the frame. Gravity will keep the plate in a closed position. To keep the plate in an open position, slide the plate up and drill a 3/8″ hole in its lower two inches, continuing the drilling through the 1/4″ plywood sealer. Use a 3/8″ dowel as a keeper. To facilitate circulation, a hole of about 4″ × 8″ should be cut in a wall of the head very close to the cabin sole and fitted with a grate. Good circulation will now be insured with the plate open, and then retention of the heat for the salon can be achieved when the plate is closed. The head can be strung with wet gear out of sight and out of mind.

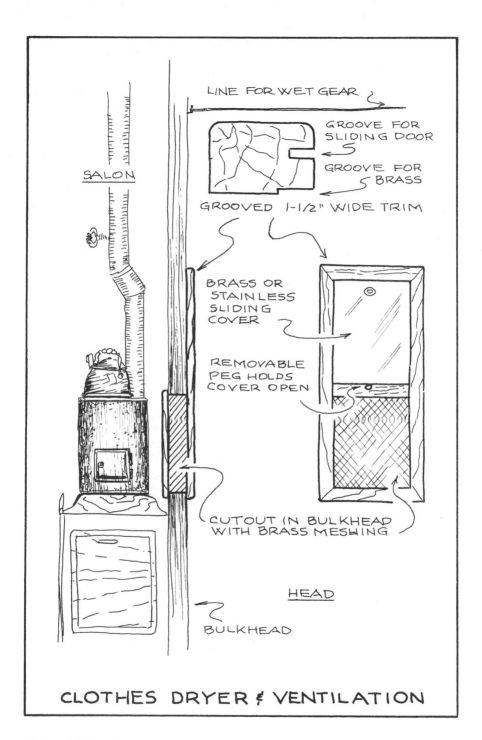

LINE FOR WET GEAR

GROOVE FOR SLIDING DOOR

GROOVE FOR BRASS

GROOVED 1-1/2" WIDE TRIM

SALON

BRASS OR STAINLESS SLIDING COVER

REMOVABLE PEG HOLDS COVER OPEN

CUTOUT IN BULKHEAD WITH BRASS MESHING

HEAD

BULKHEAD

CLOTHES DRYER & VENTILATION

CANE DOORS

Ventilation of lockers is always of primary concern, especially in steel, fiberglass, and ferro cement hulls, where much condensation forms. Solid doors, in spite of the finger holes and cutey sweety anchors routed in them, provide only pathetic little puffs of air. Something much more drastic is required. On *Warm Rain*, all the doors have inserts of woven cane, so we're able to keep all lockers mildew and condensation free. Fabricating doors is no small task, so be prepared to spend time — about an hour and a half per door.

Cut the door frames to about a 2½" width, from 13/16" stock, and assemble with single dowels in each corner using a mitre jig. Glue with resorcinol, and clamp. Wipe off all excess glue immediately or it will seep deep into the grain and cause permanent stains, removable only with an ax. Let it set overnight.

Rout a 3/16" groove 1/2" in from the frame's edge. This will accommodate 1/8" caning beads, which you can buy by the roll from furniture finishers. Rough cut a piece of cane, with at least a 3/4" overhang past the groove all the way around, and soak in warm water. Whatever you do, *do not* skip this step. The cane must soak thoroughly, and this can take up to half an hour. An eastern boat manufacturer saw the cane doors in *From A Bare Hull* and decided to put them on all his boats, but he somehow managed to miss the paragraph on soaking, and ended up with limper, saggier looking things than the mammaries of a 90-year-old African grandmother.

Lay a bead of glue clear around the groove (Elmer's glue will do), towel the cane dry, and lay it in place, making sure the pattern runs parallel to the frame. Lay in the caning bead and hammer it into place with a mallet. Next, lay in the opposite caning bead and, while stretching the cane to the utmost, hammer it into place. Do likewise with the remaining two sides, keeping as much tension on the cane as possible. Wipe off all excess glue with a damp cloth and, while the cane is still wet, trim the protruding ends with a razor knife. You can belt sand off what little stubble remains, when it's dry and stiff. When dry, spray both inside and out with non-gloss shellac to prevent moisture re-entering the cane, causing the aforementioned sag. For single doors, drill 7/8" finger holes, and bullnose. For double doors, simply attach a double-hinged cabin hook and eye. Finger holes here will be redundant, for the brass fittings are sufficient handles. Install the doors with brass hinges and watch your guests turn green with envy.

3/16" CANING GROOVE

CROSS SECTION OF FRAME

CANE DOORS

LOCK STOWAGE

Nothing has caused man more worry and agony than a boat's padlock at rest. When needed, it is never to be found. When not wanted, it's everywhere: on big toes, in wine glasses, in the garbage, or right between the cream cheese and capers in the lox and bagels.

It has caused marital flare-ups and breakdowns, and, indeed, the second-most frequent question Candace asks me after, "What on earth are you talking about now?" is "Where is the lock?!" The lock is where it wants to be. Nowhere special, but always in the place where discovery consumes at least 23 minutes.

But salvation is here. I found a simple solution to this complex dilemma aboard the ketch *Glaucus*, the only other boat at a quiet anchorage called Sturt Bay. Here is how it's done.

On a 1½" thick piece of teak, about 3" × 3", trace the shape of your lock. The body only. The tongue should always stick out to indicate whereabouts. Rout the pattern deep enough to house the body flush. Bullnose the edges of the face on the two sides and the bottom. Slightly sand the top edge. From 1/4" teak stock, cut a piece to fit the back, creating an enclosed pocket. Mounting a backless holder, that is, using a bulkhead or cabin sides as a back is a mistake. The constant in and out moving of lock will scratch the area directly above resulting in endless maintenance.

Mount with one screw on either side and plug. Locate it right next to the main hatch and use it.

A timely note on locks. The combination variety is awfully handy obviating the use of keys, which disappear at least as frequently as the locks themselves. The only drawback with this is that night time operation is difficult unless you're a bat or an owl, so placing of a flashlight in an unlocked and handy area is essential. Also, be certain that the tongue is casehardened. We had the misfortune of neglecting this small point, and were relieved of a tidy heap of equipment when someone neatly cut our pretty, but putty, padlock clear off.

3"

SPACE
ROUTED OUT
FOR LOCK

1½"

1/4" PLYWOOD BACK

LOCK STOWAGE

SLIDING DOORS

Cabinet Doors

If you desire to close off an area for storage, whether in the engine room, galley, or around the chart table, the least time consuming and least expensive method would be to fabricate a partial bulkhead and equip it with sliding doors. The doors can be of either 1/8″ plexiglass or 1/8″ veneer depending on how ugly a thing you're trying to hide.

First you will need to fit the new 1/2″ plywood bulkhead into place and secure it there using cleat stock, glue and screws. Next, mill the track for your sliding doors as shown in the illustration. Mill enough to cover the entire perimeter of your bulkhead opening, using the 1/4″ deep slotted pieces (see dotted line) for the bottom and sides, and the 1/2″ deep slotted pieces for the top. This way, you can put the sliding door in place by pushing it up into the 1/2″ slot, then dropping it down into the 1/4″ slot and still have 1/4″ of track lip on top to hold it in. So, mill the pieces and glue and screw them into place drilling from the front through the 1/2″ wide "L," then countersinking and plugging. Next, cut your sliding doors from veneer or plexiglass, making the height the size of the opening (with rails in) plus 1/2″, and the length, one-half the opening plus 1″ to allow for a slight overlap. Sand all edges lightly to avoid splintering. The simplest handle for the doors is of course the finger hole, providing it's at least 7/8″ in diameter. Anything less will result in stuck fingers and a lot of cursing.

Cabin Doors

Since few small boats have enough space for hinged doors to provide privacy, the alternative can be sliding doors. These can only be used if a clear surface exists on the bulkhead adjoining the passage to be closed off. The one disadvantage you will suffer with this system is that you'll have to put in a permanent low bulkhead (4″ will probably suffice) across the opening for your lower slide to be mounted on.

Cut your door from a piece of 1/4″ plywood and frame it with 13/16″ stock cut to 3″ width and grooved as shown. Lightly bullnose all edges, cut the corners to 45°, glue all grooves, then assemble along with plywood filler and screw diagonally across the corner joints. An occasional screw through the frame and plywood, about every 18″ or so, would be good insurance.

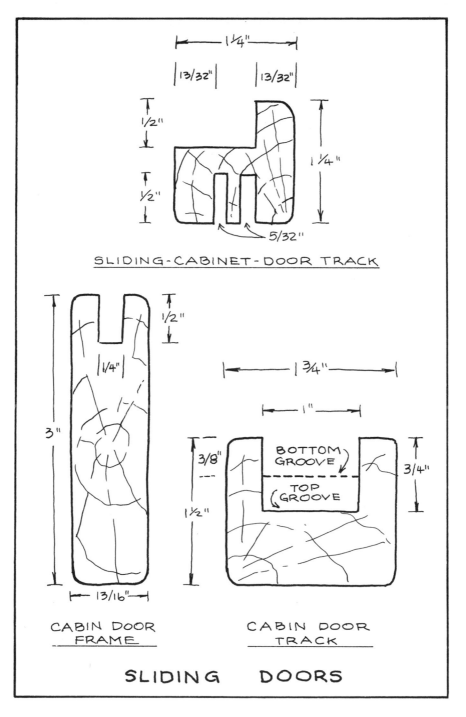

1¼"

13/32" 13/32"

½"

¼"

½"

5/32"

SLIDING-CABINET-DOOR TRACK

½"

¼"

3"

1 3/4"

1"

3/8"

BOTTOM GROOVE

TOP GROOVE

3/4"

1½"

13/16"

CABIN DOOR FRAME

CABIN DOOR TRACK

SLIDING DOORS

The track, as shown, can be milled from solid 1¾″ stock or built up of three individual layers. The groove of the upper track will be twice as deep (3/4″) as the lower track (3/8″) (see above). Cut your track to such a length as to allow 2″ overhangs past the door in both open and closed position. Glue and screw both tracks onto the bulkhead using the measurement of the finished door to determine spacing. Be certain the tracks are perfectly parallel. For stoppers, glue filler pieces into both ends of each track. Wax the tracks with good heavy wax. A candle will do.

To keep the door from sliding inadvertently, drill a 1/8″ hole through the track and door, in both closed and open positions, and insert a small removable eyebolt to hold it wherever you like.

SLIDING DOORS

LOCKER PADDING

Although I do sometimes get carried away with gadgets and tinkering, I think that locker padding is·a must in most yachts. First, it should be used to save the hull. Heavy tumbling objects, like cans, chains, wrenches, and winch handles, can gouge wood, chip paint, cause rust on steel, and crack the gelcoat on fiberglass liners. Secondly, the stowed goods should be protected. Tiny leaks will quickly cause rust, spoiling the last can of rum cake that you were just dying to bite into.

Most padding can be readily and cheaply bought, the most common type being solid heavy gauge plastic. Although the varieties and sources are limitless, we chose the rug-saver for our lockers. Often used in semi-finished buildings, where the carpets are being protected from wear, this usually comes in a 24″ width on a virtually endless roll. It's a very heavy, yet flexible, plastic sheet with nobbies on one side, and a smooth surface on the other. The nobbies are perfect for allowing air to circulate beneath the plastic, and the smooth side is easily kept clean. It is thick and rigid enough that it will remain in place even against the steepest of hulls, so no adhesion is necessary. We use it in our lockers under cans and heavy tools, and in our chain lockers, under the anchor chain. Maybe I'm over-reacting, but at 69¢ a running foot,who can afford to wait and see.

Another ideal material we've found, through a friend who works for the airlines, is an open webbing made of flexible plastic. The walls of the webs are about 1/8″ high and the diamond-shaped cells take up one-half square inch each. It makes very good padding, as well as great non-skid under plates, etc., but seems much more difficult to clean if something mucky and gooey is spilled into the tight little cells.

bibelots

INTERIOR GRABRAILS

Virtually all production boats, as well as many time-tested yachts, suffer from a lack of interior grabrails. These are an absolute must if the crew is to operate safely in a seaway.

Grabrails fall into two general categories: the traditional looped type, and the underdeck-supported solid-trough type. Both are extremely functional, and have a place belowdecks in different locations.

Trough Rails

If at all possible, most vessels should be fitted with cabin-length trough rails running along where the cabinsides join the underdecks. These rails have three major functions: a) they serve as an uninterrupted grabrail that can be clutched at any spot, b) they act as a trough for water coming in through forgotten portlights, and c) they serve as a marvelous little shelf to stuff all sorts of knickknacks into, from keys to small change.

Construction is quite basic, consisting really of an "L" of hardwood. The horizontal piece should be of 3/4" stock and have an average width of 5". Since most cabins taper toward the bow, it will be necessary to cut some of these from stock as wide as 8" or 10", depending, of course, on how drastic the curve is. I advise using templates of 1/8" plywood to eliminate experimentation with expensive hardwoods. Of the 5" width, 3" should be used to fit against the underdeck, the other two will form the bottom of the trough. The inboard edge of the support should be cut on a bevel that matches the cabin sides. In wood boats, fastening will be child's play, since you'll just be screwing into hefty hanging knees. On most fiberglass boats, underdecks have a plywood core and occasionally a secondary plywood lining. The combination of the two make for an excellent base. One must first establish the thickness of each of these (especially if only a plywood core is present) with information from the manufacturer before any drilling is begun, or one may find sunlight pouring in through the little drilled holes. With wood on wood, use glue; with wood on fiberglass, use mish-mash.

The rail itself should be ripped from 3/4" stock to a width of 2½". Bullnose all edges, and with the bottom of the rail overhanging the support by 1/2", glue and fasten with 1¼" #10 F.H.S.M. screws on 6" centres. You will probably need someone to hold the rail in place while you drill and screw, especially if the sheer of your vessel is drastic. Run a tiny bead of silicone sealer between the support and the cabin side to make the trough watertight.

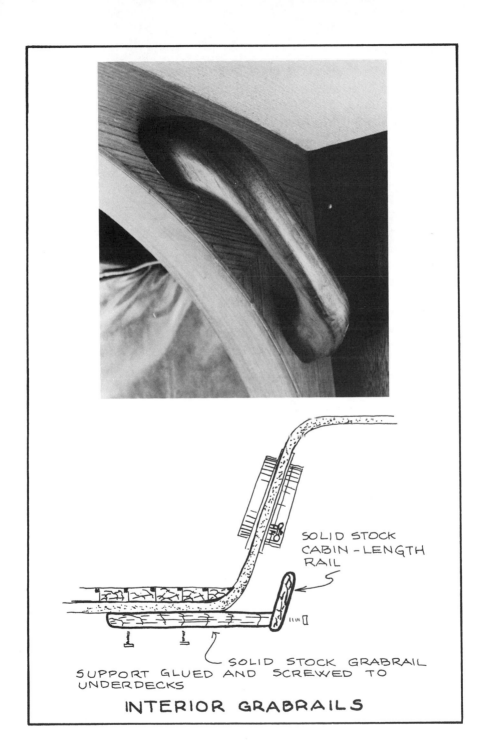

SOLID STOCK
CABIN-LENGTH
RAIL

SOLID STOCK GRABRAIL

SUPPORT GLUED AND SCREWED TO
UNDERDECKS

INTERIOR GRABRAILS

Loop Rails

Some people advocate the use of these directly overhead or about 1½' off the keel line. I feel that, in most yachts, the trough rail would be of much greater value, unless you're an ardent commuter of trains or buses who automatically reaches up for support when the going is lurchy. If so, read the section on exterior grabrails for information.

I do feel, however, that the looped rail has great value in its single loop format, around places like the sides of companionways; above difficult to get in and out of berths; in the head; and in nearly any other place in the yacht where support is needed. For up and out support, you'll just have to think hard and pretend you're in a blow; but for general location, a simple experiment involves sectioning off the cabin sole into one foot square areas, then standing in each of these, and literally throwing yourself into all imaginable directions. If it hurts, that's the place you need a single loop of grabrail.

The size of single loops should generally be determined by the space available, with the maximum loop hole of 8" length supported by 3" flat ends, tapered as in illustration. Fabrication is described under "Exterior Grabrails."

Installation should be by means of 1/4" S.S.R.H. machine screws (bolts), with flat washers and nuts for support. If this is not feasible (as in some companionways), #12 sheet metal screws can be used with generous portions of resorcinol glue. Whichever you use, be sure you don't over-tighten; few things split as easily as these damned grabrails.

GRABRAILS

BERTH CURTAINS AND PORTLIGHT CURTAINS

Perhaps I'm over the hill and consequently approaching the age where people whisper the adjective "stodgy" behind my person, but I love few things more after having a fine lunch of cheeses, smoked salmon, and a glass of wine in the solitude of a northern anchorage, than crawling into the pilot berth and catching 40 winks. It's a special little thing that divides the day into manageable halves, but it's a thing that could not be done without a well-curtained berth. Like many people, I cannot sleep with the sun blazing through my eyelids.

Since the upper part of the foot of the berth is open onto the chart table, one wing was installed as an "L". Since a 6'5" curtain rod would have looked completely terrible, we used single strand stainless wire, stretched very tightly between two padeyes, with a brass U-nail in the centre. All this is nicely hidden by the 1/2" overhang of the solid grab rail that runs the length of the cabin. One must not use multi-strand wire for curtain suspension because it can fray and cause absolute havoc with both curtain and fingers. When open, the curtains are held at either end by a sash whose two ends have been fitted with small pieces of Velcro. One end is tacked to the bulkhead. You have to try it. You haven't slept so well since you were in the cradle.

Portlight Curtains

I have never had an affinity for traditional curtains on portlights. They flip-flop nauseatingly at sea, they don't lie quite closed enough for privacy, and they seem to destroy the preciousness of beautiful bronze portlights with their bulky housiness. Of course, for non-opening large windows, they are the only solution. For others, a simple device exists that dispenses with the rods and curtain ties and can be best described as a portlight cap.

Use material that matches your cushion covers, and cut out a circular piece 1" greater in diameter than the widest dimension of your portlight. Do not neglect to include the dogs and hinges. Now cut a strip of cloth 1" longer than the circumference of the portlight (including dogs and hinges) and 1½" wider than the portlight's depth. This will be the side. Sew the side onto the circle using a 1/2" seam allowance, and hem it, leaving a space for elastic. Insert the elastic with a safety pin, and what have you got? A flat-topped shower cap. It can be quickly put on and more quickly stowed neatly inside another cap, leaving the beauty of the portlight undisturbed during the day.

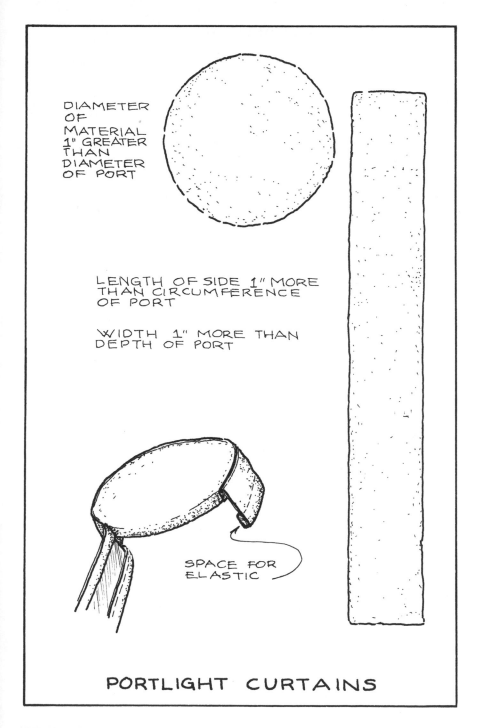

DIAMETER OF MATERIAL 1" GREATER THAN DIAMETER OF PORT

LENGTH OF SIDE 1" MORE THAN CIRCUMFERENCE OF PORT

WIDTH 1" MORE THAN DEPTH OF PORT

SPACE FOR ELASTIC

PORTLIGHT CURTAINS

BULKHEAD HAND GRAB

If your cutaway-bulkheads are not equipped with posts, that's too bad. Although this oversight can provide a boat with unbroken visual volume, you should add a bit of security to un-grabable and un-hugable space by fabricating and installing the illustrated hand grab.

For strength, a triple laminate has to be constructed. The rough size will be about 3″ × 8″. The middle piece should be the thickness of the bulkhead, and the two outside pieces, the size of the overhang of the existing trim around the bulkhead. The central piece should be end grain (in the completed hand grab), while the outside pieces should have the grain perpendicular to the central piece. Glue with resorcinol and clamp.

Cut the bulkhead trim 90°, then cut the bulkhead corner itself to a 45° angle with as clean a cut as possible, remembering that the existing trim is to remain intact (hopefully) for all but the very corner. Measure from the inside corners of the leftover trim pieces, determine the bottom length of the hand grab, then mark from these points, flaring out, following the angle of the cut trim. You will now have to rout or dado out the bottom of the piece to bulk and thickness. Dado to a depth so that the grab's base edge will meet the inside tips of the existing trim pieces.

If you have, by some saintworthy miracle, managed to follow the instructions thus far with your chunk of wood and sanity intact, take a deep breath, for you're over the hump.

Now, you'll want the hand hole itself about 4″ long and 1¼″ wide. That should accommodate even the sausagiest of fingers. The ends of the hole can taper, so on 3″ centres, cut two 1″ holes with a hole saw (leaving 1/2″ of wood on the bottom of the grab), then finish cutting out the rest of the grip with a jigsaw. To establish the cutting lines, make your lower cut parallel to the bottom of the grab; make your upper cut by scribing an arc joining the tops of the holes. Make a centre space 1¼″ wide. To get the outside radius of the hand grab, re-fit the piece, and scribe a line from the top of each old trim, following the upper curve of the fresh-cut hand hole. Cut with a jigsaw, and round all edges to match the existing trim. Glue and screw vertically into the bulkhead about an inch from the ends, and plug. Nifty, isn't it?

SEARAILS

Strangely enough, even in this day and age, when you'd think everyone would have gotten the word, many boats still arrive from the manufacturers without searails. How they expect things to remain on counters and tables in any seaway, heaven only knows.

What is probably worse than no searail at all, are the silly things made of little spindles with a toothpick of a rail along their tops. These frivolities will last through exactly the first five minutes of a good wind, until someone grabs them or leans against them, whereupon they turn instantly into kindling.

Searails should be of solid stock 13/16'' or better, 2'' high (clear), rabbetted, and screwed, and glued firmly to the countertops. If you are contemplating future alterations to your vessel, you will be well advised to mill a backlog of searails all at one time, for then you will be sure they match perfectly, since you will be performing all the milling with the same machine settings.

A much improved version of the old solid searail has been born. I first saw it on a Fast Passage 39 from Philbrook Shipyards in Sidney, B.C. They very thoughtfully incorporated grab loops into the searails, providing excellent security. These I would think to be indispensible around chart tables, galleys, heads, and engine rooms; anywhere hands may be in need of a quickly available support.

The overall height of these rails must be at least 2¾'', since the height of the hand hold should be 1 1/8'', the handle itself 3/4'', and the bottom rabbet 7/8''. Beveling the top should be bypassed in favour of the extra strength. The length of each loop hole is optional, ranging from a minimum of 5'' to accommodate most hands, to a maximum of 8'' to provide minimum strength. The solid parts between the loops can range anywhere from 2'' up. The rails should be thoroughly bullnosed with a 3/8'' bit, along the top and bottom, as well as inside the loops.

They can be installed either as in the photo, or the illustration, with open or closed corners. The closed corner has the obvious advantage of strength, but has the disadvantages of: a) restricting sweeping of counter tops, b) having nasty things lodge in the inside of the sharp corners, and c) being a pointed weapon against hips and pelvises. If properly rabbeted, glued, and screwed, the open corners can provide quite sufficient strength.

SEARAILS

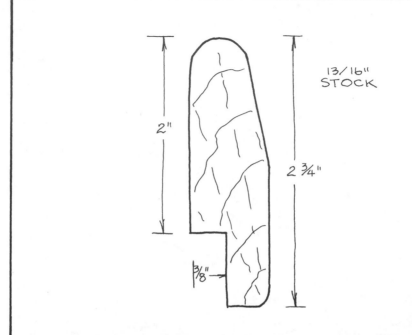

13/16"
STOCK

2"

2 ¾"

⅜"

SEARAILS

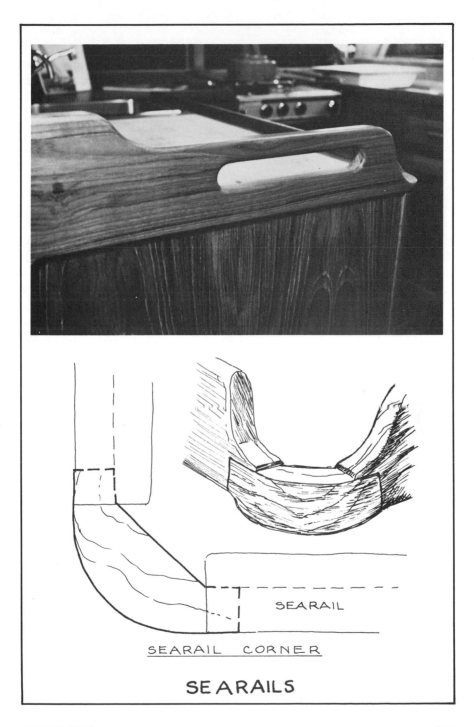

SEARAIL

SEARAIL CORNER

SEARAILS

DESK

Desks are magical places aboard a yacht. You can just sneak behind one, spread out papers and pens and, after sitting there an hour staring vacuously into space, you can come out and feel like you've actually done something. A number of people who have read *From A Bare Hull* have written asking for details about our desk (I euphemize it as my "study"), so here they are. The elevation and layout are shown in the illustrations.

To achieve comfortable foot space, a 6″ riser was built to provide a 20″ wide flat surface instead of a 14″ one. A small drop-hatch provides access to the space beneath it. The area of the desk was by the location of the bulkheads made rather claustrophobic, so we cut away the inboard upper third of the main bulkhead (the desk faces aft) opening up a very wide vista into the salon. An opening portlight in the cabinside directly over the desk, and what additional light we've gained by allowing light from the skylight to come through the cutout in the bulkhead, have turned this into a very pleasant work space. The weakening of the bulkhead through the removal of a portion of it was compensated for by the addition of a 2″ × 2″ post on the bulkheads inboard edge. Not only is this of a structural benefit, but it's also a perfect thing to grab in overreactive seas. The lower portion of the post was dadoed to allow insertion of the bulkhead into it. They were glued and screwed together. The upper end of the post was fitted under the deckbeams and secured there by means of a routed pad into which it snuggly fit. The pad was in turn glued and screwed to the deckbeams.

So now we were back where we had been before we started butchering the bulkhead, except that we had a nice flat floor. The choice to have the desk facing aft was fairly obvious for: a) the hull was turning in rather abruptly so about 25° more floor width could be gained for feet, and b) the salon was a brighter area to steal light from than the forepeak.

Next, we installed a short fore and aft 1/2″ ply bulkhead at the outboard end of the designed 28″ seat. This was secured to the main and forward bulkheads with the aid of cleat stocks and bonded (on its outboard face) to the hull. Over this bulkhead came another major structural piece in the form of a 1/2″ plywood "L" which was to become the horizontal (fixed) bottom of the desk, the armrest, and the bottom of both the bookshelf and the shallow cabinet beside it. This was tied into all three bulkheads by means of 3/4″ cleat stock, and it was supported on the inboard end with a solid teak knee cut from 2″ stock.

240   THE FINELY FITTED YACHT

The seat was fabricated from three pieces of 1/2" plywood (top, aft side, inboard side) with a drop hatch to give access to its rather spacious interior. Plywood seating cleats, 1/2" × 1½", screwed to the underside of the top kept the lid from falling through.

The rough work for the bookshelf and adjoining cabinet were next. The cabinet needed only an inboard face and an aft side, but the problematic part was to join the two pieces at 90° and end up with a presentable job. Plywood endgrain is not too shippy, and I don't really fancy "L" trim, so we decided to mill a corner piece from solid teak that would serve as a structural support for the sides and finish off the endgrain at the same time. The corner post shown was used to finish off the 3/8" plywood ends; it can be milled simply on a table saw by following the shown measurements. The short bookshelf was fitted in place and to avoid unsightly cleat stock supports, we just made sure it was a tight fit, glued the ends, then screwed into them from the other side of the bulkheads that the shelf adjoined. When screwing into the edge of plywood in this fashion, care must be taken with the amount of force used, for it's extremely easy to become over-zealous and rip out the delicate threads you've just cut.

Then the teak work on the desk was begun. The free standing corner of the desk was cut on an angle to reduce the likelihood of injury. The two sides and the front were cut from 13/16" stock, and were attached to the desk bottom with the aid of cleat stock. The narrow fixed piece of the top (from which the lid is hinged) was put in in a similar fashion.

The frame for the lid was made up of five 3" wide pieces, using lapped joints. A groove was routed in the bottom of the frames so a 3/8" plywood could be let in and glued in place. Another piece of 3/8" was used to fill in the space to within 1/16" of the tops of the frames. The last 1/16" was filled with leather to form a very excellent writing surface. The leather was laid in with contact cement (starting in one corner to eliminate wrinkles) and pressed firmly down with a cotton-gloved hand to avoid staining. Round hinges were recessed into the lid and the fixed piece of the top. A small cabin hook was affixed to the outboard edge of the lid to keep it hooked to the underdeck if extensive, two-handed rummaging is required inside the desk. A brass lamp provides good reading light.

It's such a cozy nook I almost never leave it.

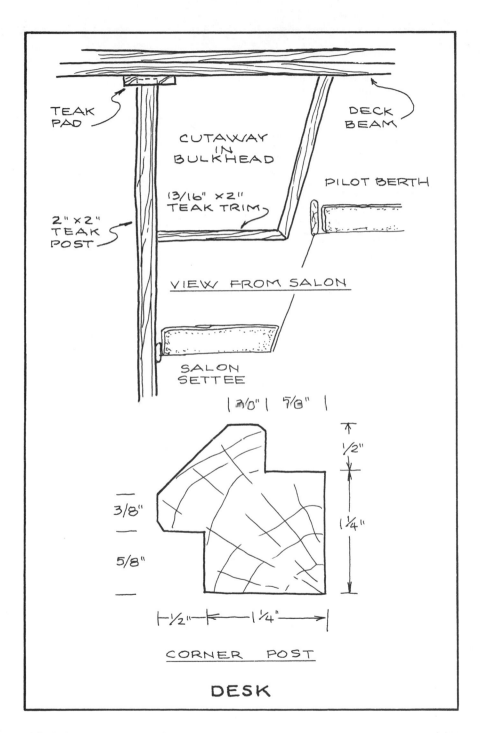

TEAK
PAD

DECK
BEAM

CUTAWAY
IN
BULKHEAD

PILOT BERTH

13/16" × 2"
TEAK TRIM

2" × 2"
TEAK
POST

VIEW FROM SALON

SALON
SETTEE

3/0" 5/8"

1/2"

3/8"

1¼"

5/8"

½" 1¼"

CORNER POST

DESK

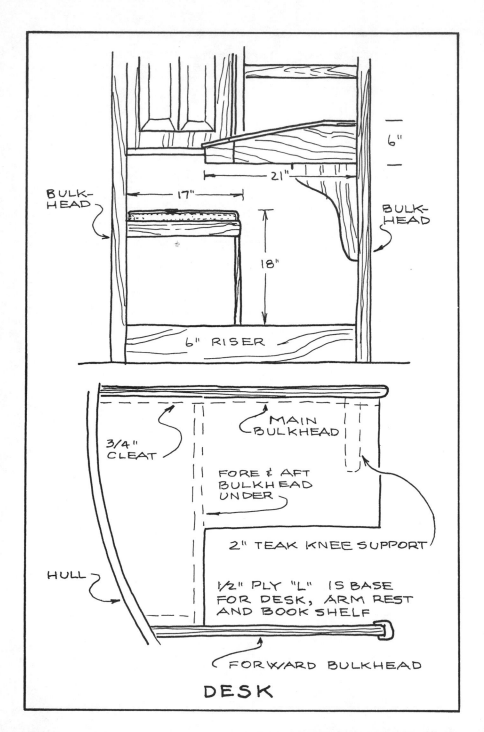

6"

21"

BULK-
HEAD

17"

18"

BULK-
HEAD

6" RISER

3/4"
CLEAT

MAIN
BULKHEAD

FORE & AFT
BULKHEAD
UNDER

2" TEAK KNEE SUPPORT

1/2" PLY "L" IS BASE
FOR DESK, ARM REST
AND BOOK SHELF

HULL

FORWARD BULKHEAD

DESK

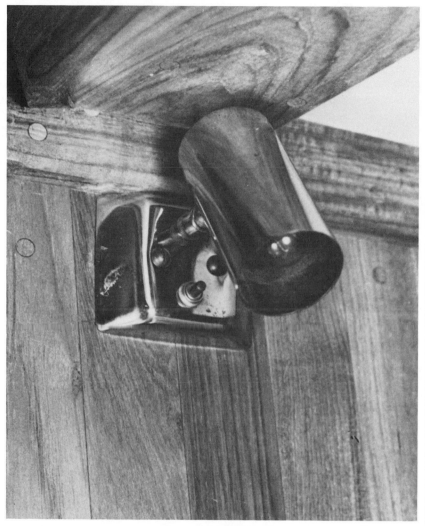

Brass reading lamp with high intensity 12 volt bulb. About 4″ high.

THROUGH-HULL PLUGS

All cruising and racing boats should have plugs aboard, for neither is immune to failed seacocks. Indeed, many offshore racers are required to carry them as standard safety equipment. It would not seem overcautious to have at least two plugs for each size of seacock just in case trouble really does come in threes.

Only softwood should be used for plugs. I have heard the tragic tale of a hard-as-steel oak plug which, when driven into the seacock by an overanxious crew, split the housing like a blooming rose; so use softwood (cedar is perfect), and use your head. If you have no access to a lathe, fret not, an hour's whittling will supply you with 50 years worth of plugs. For the large ones, cut 5″ long plugs from 1½″ stock, tapering them from 1½″ to 3/4″. After your first two cuts, it would be nice to place the plug into a vise (fat end only) so that two more tapering cuts can be made with a jigsaw. Next, get out the shoe rasp and rasp away. If your wood is well chosen, rounding the plug with a rasp should not be too demanding. Round the ends to avoid splintering. Drill a 1/4″ hole through the fat end and run a generous lanyard through it. With this the plug can be tied to the seacock it is to serve, for both storage and as a safety line to hold it in place if the need ever arises. When needed (heaven forbid), just tap the plug into place and wrap the lanyard around the base of the seacock (or the greasing plug and seacock handle) to keep the water motion from spitting the plug back out.

For smaller seacocks (3/4″), cut your plug from 1″ cedar (the 1″ is minimum), make it 4″ long, and taper it to 3/8″. Inspect plugs each year for checking or cracking. A little oil now and then wouldn't hurt.

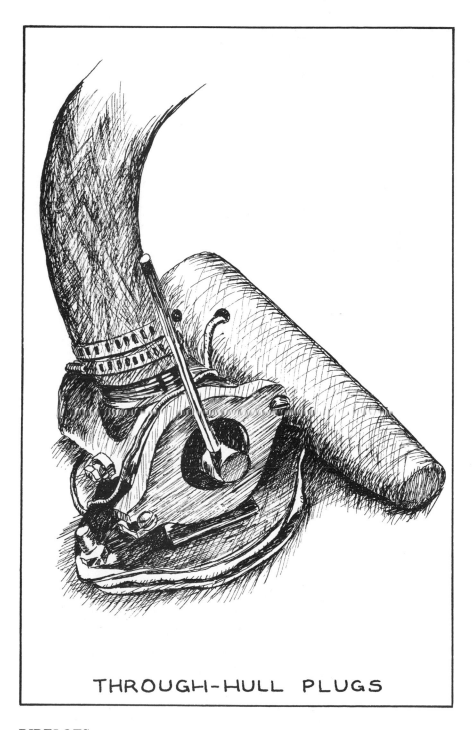

THROUGH-HULL PLUGS

COMPANIONWAY LADDER

Warm Rain's original design called for a companionway equipped with a number of slide out, lift up, yank away steps, all of which, when removed to make way to the engine room, made into a pile of rubble over which one constantly tripped. In other words, it didn't work worth a damn.

Every effort should be made on a yacht to abandon all overcomplicated hybrids, and the companionway is a good place to start. The traditional ladder is the ultimate solution. Its lovely rigid sides can house any number of hand holes, and with the help of some fine hinges at the top and a snap shackle on a short lanyard below the bottom rung, it can be swiftly lifted up out of the way and made fast to a padeye on a deck beam.

The sides of the ladder should be cut from 13/16″ stock, to a width of no more than 6″. If the ladder is sloped even just a little, very comfortable 7″ wide rungs can be fitted to the 6″ sides. If space demands, 4″ wide sides are tolerable. Radius the tops of the sides pleasantly, as shown. Draw in your treads allowing for 13/16″ stock. They should be spaced as far apart as you can conveniently make them (13″ is not excessive), remembering that the farther your rungs are spread, the easier it will be to come down the ladder facing forward. The tread length (ladder's interior width) need not be more than 12″. Dado in the space for your rungs on each side (not forgetting to mark the inside surfaces of the sides first) with your dado blades set at 3/8″. Check your setting on a piece of scrap wood before you cut the ladder.

Now, with your table saw blade set on the same angle as your ladder slope, trim the forward and aft edges of your rungs to match. Now, set your router at a depth of 7/8″ and rout a 1½″ × 4½″ hand hole near the top of each side. (A drill and jigsaw can be substituted for the router. See "Boarding Ladder".) For young sailors, a second set of hand holes can be cut between the second and third rungs. Bullnose the hand holes and edges of the ladder sides except: within 1/2″ of the rung slots, the footings, and the area where the hinges are to fit. Assemble the ladder with plastic resin glue and two or three 1″ #10 P.H.S.M. screws per rung end. When the glue has set, attach the hinges to the ladder, install the snap shackle and padeye, and lock the bottom of the ladder up to the deck beam, and have a friend hold the top of the ladder in position while you screw the hinges to the aft face of the cabin.

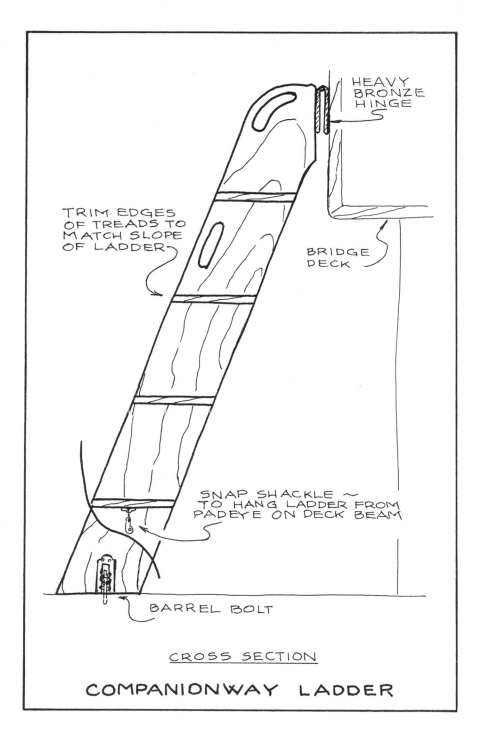

HEAVY
BRONZE
HINGE

TRIM EDGES
OF TREADS TO
MATCH SLOPE
OF LADDER

BRIDGE
DECK

SNAP SHACKLE ~
TO HANG LADDER FROM
PADEYE ON DECK BEAM

BARREL BOLT

CROSS SECTION

COMPANIONWAY LADDER

FOREPEAK DESK CONVERSION

Many vessels have spacious forepeaks which, with a small crew, are mostly unused or worse, become a junk mine for rummage sale organizers. One of the better ways of eliminating this waste is to eliminate one berth, and install in its place, a desk-cum-storage area.

First, determine how wide you'll want your desk top — 20" seems minimal, over 36" on anything smaller than the Queen Mary seems obscene. At the determined point, cut out your berth face and top with a jig saw. Remove all old cleat stock that supported the pieces you've just cut out by digging out the plugs, unscrewing the screws, then *gently* prying the cleats away with a chisel. Gently. This is a minor remodeling job, *not* a housewrecking.

If there is bonding to be cut, remove the blade from your hacksaw, wrap one end with tape so the teeth won't gnaw away your milk-toast palm, then, after cutting a starting hole with an *old* chisel, proceed to cut along the bond as close to the hull as possible. To insure that the hull will remain unmarred, wrap a piece of tape around the last two inches of the tip of the blade as well.

To close off what's left of the berth, install a full-height 1/2" thick bulkhead (see Chapter 14 of *Bare Hull*) establishing the inboard edge 1" inboard of the berth face. To trim, rip a 1½" piece of teak or mahogany to a 1½" width. Dado a 1/2" wide by 3/4" deep dado into it. Bullnose all four edges with a 3/8" bullnose bit.

Put glue into the dado, then slip the trim onto the bulkhead and screw to the bulkhead edge. One screw every 18" is plenty. Countersink and plug.

Next, from 3/4" plywood, cut and fit a desk top using the same scribing and cutting procedure as you did for the bulkhead. To speed things along with the fitting, it may be prudent to install the cleats on which the top is finally to rest, at this time. Three-quarter-inch cleat stock glued and screwed to each bulkhead will be fine. If your desk top is no wider than 30", you will not need to support it on the hull; cleats on the bulkheads alone will suffice. When installing the cleats, remember the cabin sole-to-desk distance must be at least 26". When measuring this height, do so halfway between the outboard and inboard edges of the top so that the curvature of the hull will be taken into consideration. If you don't, you may end up writing in a dead-man's float position.

Glue and screw the cleats onto the bulkheads. Fit the desk top into place but *do not* install it. Remove it to a nice open working space and cover it with whatever surfacing material you like: wood,

THE FINELY FITTED YACHT

FOREPEAK DESK CONVERSION

formica, leather, etc. (see Chapter 18 of *Bare Hull*). Do all the edge finishing, then lay glue over your cleats and drop the top into place. Drill and screw from below, taking care to mark the drill bit with a piece of tape so that you won't drill too far and come through the top. Next, trim out the inboard edge. If you've fabricated the corner as shown in the illustration, i.e. well rounded, it will be most economical to use three separate pieces of 13/16″ or 1½″ teak milled to a 2″ wide "L", with a 3/8″ × 3/4″ (or 3/4″ × 3/4″) cut out. Putting searails on a desk is the height of folly, for it will create an unbearable writing surface unless you have well notched lower arms.

The corner piece will take a lot of hand fitting but it will look beautiful. Install it unfinished, that is, not trimmed down to final thickness. You can file and sand it once it's glued into place. Holding the thing while the glue sets is no small feat. You'll have to screw a small cleat temporarily to the bottom of the desk against which a C clamp can bite. You may of course invest in an esoteric little tool (see photo) called an edging clamp, which will be valuable if you're doing other moulding trim on tables or bulkhead edges, but it does cost over six dollars, so if it's for a one-time use, use a temporary cleat with a C clamp and to hell with professionalism.

To augment the desk, cabinets or bookshelves can be installed above it, with a directional reading light (not the dome light that Candace is trying to mislead you with in her illustration). If the forward hatch is solid, one should contemplate installing a deadlight in it for more natural light.

The space forward of the new bulkhead can nicely incorporate a net-shelf to house bedding, sails, etc.

Now, a minor detail. Since neither reading nor writing has made any great inroads as a stand-up sport, effort should be made to fabricate a modest, yet comfortable, seat. The most functional would seem to be one that hinges up from the face of the remaining berth. It can be about 16″-18″ wide and 13″ deep at its shallowest point; it can be cut from 3/4″ plywood and upholstered with sturdy fabric. To support the seat in its horizontal position, two hinged knees should be fitted below it. These hinge "under" when needed as supports and hinge "out" of the way against the seat bottom when not. To make space for them when the seat is folded down, cut a hole in the face of the berth. The hole width must equal the distance between the pins of the hinges at the two knees, and no more. The very edges of the hole will be supporting the knees when the seat is opened up. To make sure all these hinged beasts are kept from flapping madly about at sea, install a tiny barrel bolt on the berth face and have its shaft slip into a hole drilled into the seat. (Elbow catches or bayonets will do almost as well.) To be sure all will remain intact, use only piano hinges, and to stop the knees from "slipping" out from below the seat, let two 3/8" dowels into the end of each knee allowing them to protrude about 3/8". Round their tips. Drill corresponding holes into the berth face into which the dowels can slip.

There. Now, sit down and write your dearest a letter. Momma will love ya for it.

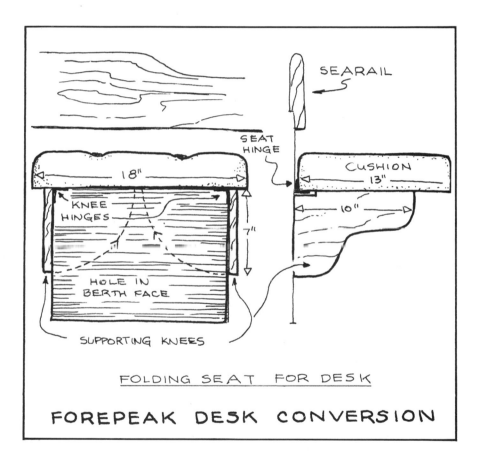

FOLDING SEAT FOR DESK

FOREPEAK DESK CONVERSION

DEADLIGHTS AND PRISMS

It seems that no one in the history of sail has ever had enough natural light in his vessel. This is especially true of ocean cruising and racing boats whose vulnerable glass surfaces have to be kept to a minimum, resulting in black holes of Calcutta below decks. Fortunately, designers have lately been rediscovering deadlights as practical alternatives.

Deadlights in decks, cabin tops, hatches, or drop-boards transmit wonderful quantities of light through relatively small areas. They fall under three general types: traditional deadlights, prisms, and fiberglass light spots.

Traditional Deadlights

Here, I speak of the bronze-rimmed, heavy-glassed, non-opening ports, which can be purchased at better marine stores. Ranging in size from 3″ to 8″ in glass diameter, they are easy to install in cabin tops, hatches and dropboards. Their major flaw for decks and cabin tops is that the thick brass rims remain forever toe stubbers and sole scrapers. In wood decks and hatches, the problem is not totally unsolvable, for the rim can be let in flush by routing the wood surface and bedding the port in polysulphide. If this method is chosen, a 3/16″ square channel should be routed all around the rim to provide space for a decent bead of caulking. In fiberglass decks and cabin tops, you'll have no choice but to mount the port on top of the fiberglass. Since most cabin tops and decks are plywood core reinforced, and since most deadlights come without interior finishing rings, the simplest method of providing an acceptable finish would be to bullnose the cut plywood edge and hope for the best.

Two areas where the use of deadlights should be avoided are the hull and often-walked surfaces. Deadlights in the hull will tend to condense horribly in cold waters where they're constantly buffetted by cold spray. If placed in often-walked surfaces, they become dangerously loose footings when wet.

Prism Deck Lights

When copious quantities of light are required in a specific area a prism-type deadlight can be used. These come in two basic shapes: rectangular, with a lens that looks like a wedge, and round, in which case the lens looks something like an orange squeezer. They both come with brass outer frames, and both transmit and distribute light

DECK PRISMS

fabulously. The prisms are infinitely more resistant to breaking than the straight glass types and of course infinitely more expensive.

Fiberglass Light Spots

One of the cleverest methods of transmitting light below decks in a fiberglass boat is to leave off the gelcoat from an area of fiberglass and leave out the reinforcing plywood or foam core below. This method has the great advantage of not disturbing the boat's outer surfaces, thereby eliminating potential leaks and foot damage. Belated conversion is not difficult but it does take forethought.

Having ascertained that both the inside and outside of the future light spot are free from fittings, wires, etc., tape off the area topsides and sand off the coloured gelcoat. Clean with acetone and re-gelcoat with clear gel.

In the interior, carefully measure the location using beams, mast supports, etc. for verification,and draw in the area of interior liner to be removed. Remember that a very small area, say $4''$ diameter, will seem down below as if a spotlight has been turned on, so there is no need in removing acres of plywood, thereby jeopardizing the structural integrity of the deck.

Next. If you can't find out from the manufacturer the thickness of the deck core, you'll have to explore. Take a $1/8''$ drill bit and with your drill motor on low speed,begin drilling. (The more prudent might use a hand drill for this occasion.) Most cores (plywood, balsa, foam) are much softer than the fiberglass, so with a little attentiveness, you will be able to tell when you've passed through them. But do be careful and pay attention. If you're a klutz, drill in $1/32''$ at a time, then pull out the bit and see if you have brown sawdust or white fiberglass. Drill until you hit the glass, then stop. Having thus fathomed the depth, set your router with a straight bit at that depth,and clean out the whole area. A thorough man would now replace the removed core with a layer of fiberglass mat and cloth.

If considerable condensation is encountered, a thin piece of plexiglass can be cut to shape, and installed with a strip of weather proofing foam around the inner surface of its perimeter. This will create a handsome air pocket and eliminate condensation.

Whichever of the three methods you use, the results will be remarkable; you'll be forever reaching for your sunglasses.

THE FINELY FITTED YACHT

An 8″ diameter area where gelcoat has been removed lights up the belowdecks like a spotlight.

DRIP CATCHER

I have yet to see an opening portlight on a yacht that does not somehow manage to collect just enough water to viciously soak your favourite pillow upon opening. *Warm Rain's* portlights, I think, hold the unchallenged world record in this department. During a common drizzle lasting no more than a half hour, they are able to collect enough water to drown your average family of four *plus* the dog. They were helped to attain such heights by their idiotic owner who insisted to the church bell foundry that they make his portlight sleeves extra deep to keep out the blazing tropical sun. I have since spent many hours trying to figure out a way to hack off the bloody sleeves without having to tear out the whole portlight.

Where was I? Right. I found a very pleasant solution to the drip problem on a rather famous vessel, the St. Roche, a gaff schooner of 320 tons, built in 1928 especially for Arctic service. She was the first ship to navigate the Northwest Passage, a feat accomplished under the command of H.A. Larsen of the R.C.M.P. in 1940-42, a feat mostly designed to establish Canadian supremacy over the Arctic Ocean.

Take a piece of 1½" stock cut to a width of 2" and length of about 4", and hollow out a part of it with a fair whittling knife, as if you were building the port half of a dugout canoe. Bullnose the outside edges with a 3/8" bullnose and attach just under the portlights (see diagram) using a bead of silicone sealer to make it water tight, and a couple of countersunk #8 screws to hold it in place. Alternately, you can substitute plastic resin glue for the silicone, and, by opening the portlight, you can make room for a C clamp to hold the trough in place until the glue sets. Be sure to wipe off any dribbles with a damp cloth.

Not only will these little troughs make excellent water catchers, but they're also perfect little storage places for sextant box keys, ignition keys, rings, nuts and bolts and little stuff you find in your pants pocket just when you have to heave them into the laundry. Just think, a veritable tiny treasure chest under each portlight.

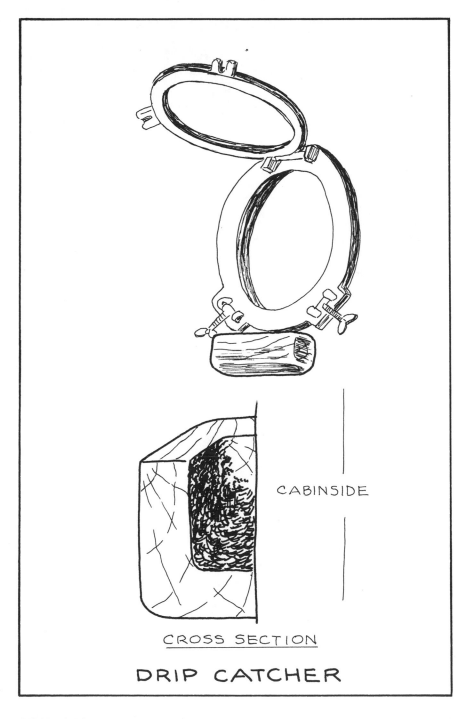

CABINSIDE

CROSS SECTION

DRIP CATCHER

INSTRUMENT COVER BOXES

All cabin face-mounted instruments, whose backs protrude into the cabin, should have boxes built to protect them and keep them out of sight. The best solution is a hinged box, giving ready access for repair and cleaning. If the whole box is hinged, the need for painstaking door fabrication is eliminated. It should be built as shallow as possible to take up as little cabin volume as necessary, and the hinges should be placed on the bottom so it hinges down and rests with its open side up. This way tools, parts, etc. can be laid into a safe and accessible place while work on the instrument is underway.

Since very little strain will ever be placed on such a box, a light construction of $1/2''$ teak or mahogany stock will be quite sufficient. If at all possible, a single box should be made to cover all instruments. This task will of course be made easier if forethought was given to placement of the instruments.

If the instruments are up high, that is, close to the overhead, construction of a three-sided, bottomless box should be contemplated, for then it can be closed tight against the overhead. Of course you will have to side-hinge such a box, but then that's a small price to pay for purity of design.

For the sake of simplicity, construct the box with all parallel sides, then hold it in place, scribe in the angle of the cabin top, then just run it through a band saw and cut the whole thing at once, taking care not to run through any screws.

The assembly of the box can be done with resorcinol glue and #8 or #6 F.H. screws. Butt ending will of course be satisfactory, unless you wish to use your dove-tailing jig and do a masterful job.

To secure the box in the closed position, a barrel bolt can be attached to the cabin side and a corresponding hole can be drilled in the box, eliminating the need for the brass end fitting. Of course if you prefer, there's always the ol' hook and eye.

One word of caution — these little boxes are irresistible hiding places for junior's secret little toys like old keys and magnets, both of them very dangerous when stuck only a few inches from a compass. Just remember the old adage: "Spare the rod, and you'll run aground."

INSTRUMENT COVER BOXES

THERMOS MOUNT

I customarily react quite adversely to gadgets, but this one, seemingly very sensible, forces me to recall all those lovely cups of tea and hot chocolate that I've missed on cool night watches simply because I couldn't face the prospect of going below and digging out the thermos from its hiding place where it had been wedged so it wouldn't roll about, then hanging on with my feet while I unscrewed the thermos lid, held the cup, spilled the stuff, rescrewed the lid, etc.

This little invention allows one to perform the whole operation with one hand. It consists of a stainless steel bracket very much like the one that holds fire extinguishers to bulkheads, a bulkhead mounted holder for mugs or cups, and a threaded plastic spigot which fits most vacuum bottles with #4 stoppers. The removal of the thermos itself can also be done with one hand, so the only tricky activity remaining would be the initial pouring of the hot fluids into the bottle.

The whole thing seems to be such a good idea that thought should be given to having two sets of mounting brackets and cup supports aboard, one located somewhere in the galley, companionway area, the other placed brilliantly in a locker accessible from the cockpit, or if such a beast doesn't exist, then in the cockpit itself. But since both brackets are rather on the frail side, i.e. not expressly designed to be stepped on, or kicked, or bashed with winch handles, thought should be given to perhaps building a little niche in the cockpit wall. As previously mentioned, much unused space usually exists around a cockpit, so why not utilize it shrewdly. For construction, see "Winch Handle Holders."

I could think of few things nicer on a cold starry night than just reaching out, flipping the little spout, and coming back with a steaming cup of something, all without having released the tiller for an instant. Besides, the niche could be a nice place to keep things like beer cans and juice glasses in the daytime. Salut.

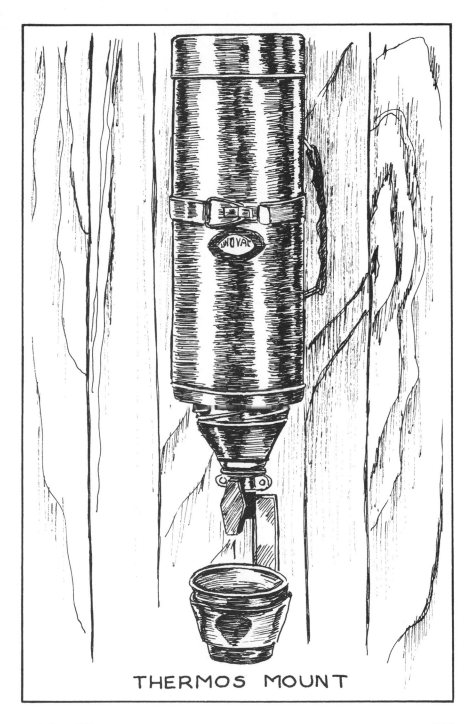

THERMOS MOUNT

THE METAMORPHOSING DOOR

It must be true that there's no better teacher than experience, for it cannot be coincidence that *Wanderer IV* has so many novel, but totally practical, ideas. One of the best the Hiscocks have devised is their cabin door for all seasons. Since their centre cockpit is rather deep, entrance to the main cabin is gained through a door that's over two feet high. An opening of such a size is a tremendous potential source of both light and air, but then, it must also be protected effectively in violent weather.

Their solution was to have the door built up from a sturdy frame, using 1″ solid stock cut to 2 3/8″ widths. The corners were overlapped. A 1/2″ wide by 1/4″ deep groove was let into the inner edge of the frame. Into this groove can be laid either a piece of plexiglass or a sheet of mosquito netting, either of which can be held in place by strips of teak molding held on by woodscrews (see diagram). So this way, in a warm buggy climate, the mosquito screen can be unrolled and, in cold cloudy climates, the plexiglass can be slipped into place.

At sea, both such delicate conveniences can be stowed (the plexiglass would love to live in an old pillowcase where it can't be scratched), and a single piece of 1/2″ thick plywood (varnished of course) could be slipped into the frame over some not too sticky bedding compound like dolfinite, then screwed down directly to the frame by-passing the moulding all together.

As an extra precaution whose necessity is brought about by the largeness of the door, *Wanderer IV* is equipped with simple, but sturdy, gallows just inside the door into which a solid wood bar can be slipped to reinforce the door, should the yacht be overtaken by heavy seas.

In all, this is a most practical idea for cruisers who spend extended periods in greatly varying climates.

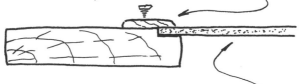

MOULDING ONLY SCREWED,
NOT GLUED, TO DOOR FRAME

PLEXIGLASS OR
MOSQUITO SCREEN

THE METAMORPHOSING DOOR

INSECT SCREENS

In the dead silence of the night when you slip away to slumber, they come humming and buzzing around your eyes and around your ears, and you slap and swat and swear and scream. Such a waste of good dreams.

Every yacht in any latitude must have insect screens. I have come to this conclusion after battling sandflies in Costa Rica, man-eating mosquitoes off the B.C. coast, and goat flies, the kind that lay eyes in the corners of your eyes, in Hawaii.

Companionway

Whether drop boards or doors are used, the method is the same. From 1/4″ solid teak, rip two 2″ wide pieces. The length should be equal to the height of the outboard sides of your drop boards or doors. Now, also from 1/4″ stock, rip two 1″ wide pieces equal in length to the lower and upper width of the opening of the companionway. With four 1/4″ wing nuts and bolts, assemble the frame, making sure the holes in the vertical pieces are centred near the inboard edges. An aggregate of two 1/4″ boards plus a wing nut will not fit into the slot made for the drop boards. I have been told that strips of Velcro will do nicely in place of wing nuts, since the frame is of such light construction. Next, stretch plastic mosquito netting over the frame, allowing it to hang 1″ past the *backs* of the sides, cut the corners away as shown in drawing and sew open-ended tunnels on all four sides, into which the wooden frame can slip piece by piece. This will enable you to disassemble, roll up the screen and stow in a very small place.

Hatches

As simple as wetting the bed, my dear grandfather used to say. Cut a piece of plastic screening to overhang your hatch openings by 3″, hem 1″ each side, sew the corners, and slip in a piece of elastic. When needed, just slip it over the hatch opening just like a shower cap. To stow, wrinkle it up like a dirty sock and throw it in some corner. Now why didn't you think of that?

Portlights

Bend ten gauge or heavier solid copper wire to snugly fit into the ports. Overlap the ends 1/2″, hammer flat, and solder. Fold brass screening over the ring, allowing it to overlap in the back by 1/2″,

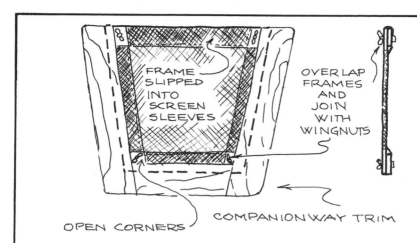

FRAME SLIPPED INTO SCREEN SLEEVES

OVERLAP FRAMES AND JOIN WITH WINGNUTS

OPEN CORNERS

COMPANIONWAY TRIM

FOR COMPANIONWAYS

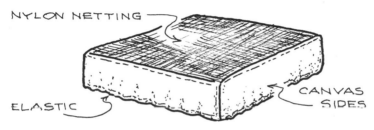

NYLON NETTING

ELASTIC

CANVAS SIDES

FOR SKYLIGHTS AND OPENING HATCHES

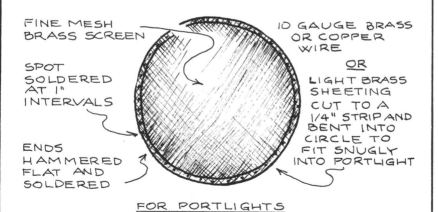

FINE MESH BRASS SCREEN

SPOT SOLDERED AT 1" INTERVALS

ENDS HAMMERED FLAT AND SOLDERED

10 GAUGE BRASS OR COPPER WIRE

OR

LIGHT BRASS SHEETING CUT TO A 1/4" STRIP AND BENT INTO CIRCLE TO FIT SNUGLY INTO PORTLIGHT

FOR PORTLIGHTS

INSECT SCREENS

and solder it every $1''$ with a small spot to the ring. Slip it into the portlight sleeve,and leave it there until it rots.

Note: nylon netting does break down after prolonged exposure to the sun. Since it is so inexpensive, one would do well to carry a small roll of it on long voyages. If nothing else, you can trade it in Bora Bora with some poor bug-chewed fool, who is desperately trying to make screens out of his wife's pantyhose and some old ladles. Don't be greedy. Her gold earrings and diamond ring should do.

THE FINELY FITTED FAN

A yacht is a wonderful place when sea and land breezes eddy in the cabin, but when the winds die and the sun beats down, things can become depressingly hot. I was aboard a yacht once in Puerto Vallarta when the wind died and the air just hung there as if it were nailed to the bulkheads, and the entire belowdecks turned quickly into a steam bath. Because of the modest interior volume of most yachts, overcoming this uncomfortable condition can be done with the help of a low drain, no noise, 12V electric fan.

Ready-made models are available from most automotive supply stores, but their great drawback is that they were designed for non-marine use, hence, their delicate metal parts can corrode rapidly to the point where the little motor will seize up. Aside from that, the little critters are, as a rule, quite unattractive.

A small shippy model can be fabricated for just a few dollars using a small electric train motor, available from most hobby shops, or from junior's model train set. If he complains that his little engine doesn't run anymore, tell him to get a rubber band. When selecting the motor, look for a plastic or aluminum housing, and ask for the quietest one they have. Tell them what you'll be using it for, so they can then give you the one that's best sealed.

The blades for the fan can be made from either thin brass sheeting or teak stock milled down to 1/8″ thickness. In both cases, the central mount would be brass.

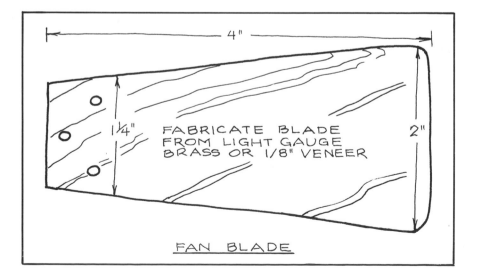

FAN BLADE

To fabricate the central mount, cut a piece of brass into the shape in Diagram A. Cut a pattern first from paper. Scribe in the 1″ diameter circle, then draw in the arms as shown. Drill 7/8″ diameter holes in each arm for mounting the blades, plus a hole in the centre of the mount for the motor shaft. Next, insert one blade at a time into a vise, bringing the dotted line even with the tops of the jaws, then hold the central part of the mount, just along the edge of the circle, with a pair of pliers (see diagram) and twist without changing the plane of the pliers, very gently and evenly until the small triangle between the vise jaws and the plier jaws is in a nearly horizontal position. This will give the arm about a 25° pitch which is quite ideal for moving air. Continue to twist each arm in the same way, making small adjustments as you go to give each arm an identical pitch. Next, cut your blades from either brass or teak to the shape in the diagram. The dimensions will give you an overall fan diameter of 9″. If this is impractically large for your boat, by all means shorten each blade an inch. You will still have ample air movement for now your engine rpm's will increase.

The most ideal place to mount the fan would be directly in front of an open portlight. To accomplish this, fabricate a hinged mount (see "Hinged Fathometer Mount" for details). The best portlight would be one on the aft cabin face to set up a good wind tunnel in the cabin. From this location, you can run the wires nicely concealed beneath the bridge deck to the breaker panel. Use a combination breaker on-off switch or a simple toggle switch. If a solar-charger panel is installed aboard, the fan can be hooked directly into it.

Bring on the mint juleps.

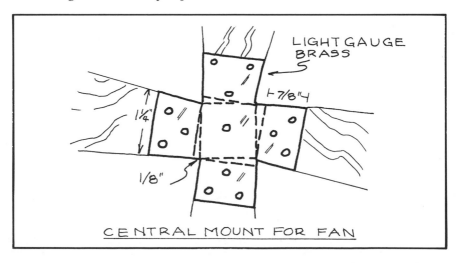

LIGHT GAUGE BRASS

CENTRAL MOUNT FOR FAN

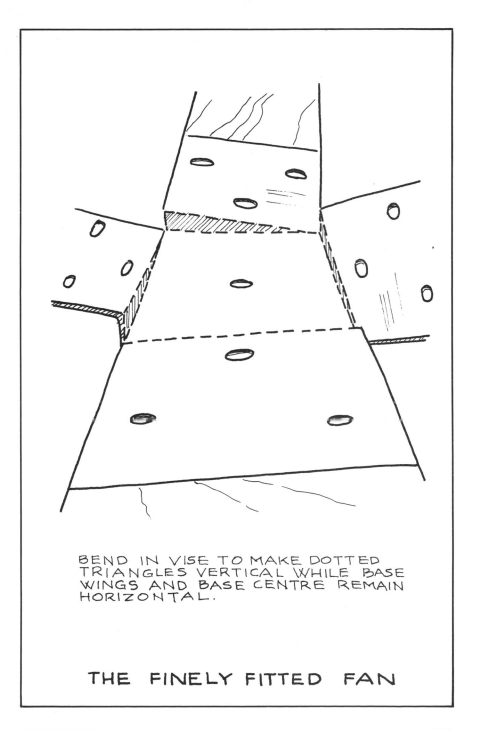

BEND IN VISE TO MAKE DOTTED
TRIANGLES VERTICAL WHILE BASE
WINGS AND BASE CENTRE REMAIN
HORIZONTAL.

THE FINELY FITTED FAN

INSULATION

One common complaint of all fiberglass boat owners is that their hulls "sweat". This condition is more aggravated in colder climates where condensation is more frequent, due to the great temperature difference between the heated interior and the very cold exterior.

Many excellent thermal insulators are available to boat builders and each has its own very valuable place.

Styrene

This material is a very good insulator. A half-inch of styrene has the "K Factor" (insulative quality) of two inches of common house insulating glass wool. It is easy to cut with a sharp "exacto" knife and a metal straight edge. It's very light, quite inexpensive (about 20¢ a square foot), and very uncomplicated to attach. Any common tile cement applied to a few critical spots will hold it in place until a hard covering of wood liner is laid over. It is perfect to lay onto a hull, cabin side, or cabin top where tongue-and-groove or plywood can be used to cover and protect it. It is most impracticable inside cabinets or in a place where no protection over it is planned, because even a paternal tap with a can of anchovies will cause a rivulet of cascading foam chips. Such an accident is messy and affects the life span of the foam quite adversely.

·To cover over styrene with either plywood or solid wood strips requires some ribbing to which one can fasten the covering wood. Two methods can be used for ribbing, one a little more expensive, the other quite dumb because it consumes a tremendous number of hours.

The Dumb Way

— rip 3/4″ plywood into 1½″ wide strips
— cut to 24″ lengths
— run it through a table saw with the blade set so high that it will cut all but the last two layers of veneer
— slit in this fashion at 1″ intervals
— mix a batch of mish-mash and using a putty knife squeeze it into the cracks. Leave a judicious layer over the rest of it.
— acetone hull where rib is to fit, then fit it into place. It should bend easily. Now the only problem is holding it there. Brace it, however, with whatever you can until the mish-mash goes off.

When using mish-mash the catalyst must be stirred into the resin first, then the asbestos or whatever, added. It is advisable to practice

THE FINELY FITTED YACHT

on a small quantity until you ascertain the amounts of catalyst you require.

Once the mish-mash has gone off, bond at least one layer of mat type over the rib just to be sure. You can nail or screw into the ribs as well as slip 1/2″ sheets of styrene in between them. The centres need not be more than 18″ if you are using 3/8″ plywood or tongue-and-groove. If you are butting slats without any tongue-and-groove or other overlap, use 12″ centres.

Decks and cabin tops usually have a plywood core for stiffness; thus the ribs can be fastened with screws while the mish-mash is going off so that awkward bracing won't be required.

The More Expensive Way

In the same fashion that you scribe plywood to fit the hull, scribe ribs out of 1¾″ stock of fir, mahogany, or other easily workable wood. Ribs may have to be cut from as wide as 6″ stock if the hull's curvature is drastic. Because once cut out these ribs have no tension forcing them straight, mish-mashing and bracing can be bypassed. A single layer of mat will bond them to the hull quite securely. You can fabricate your ribs to the thickness of styrene you wish to use.

Needless to say, I did our ceiling the dumb way. That's why I know it so well.

Rigid Urethane Foam

To insulate the rest of the hull, inside the cabinets, etc. is a grueling two-day job, but it may save mildewed clothes and soaked underwear. I at first thought it a simple matter, believing it feasible, economical, and rapid, to simply spray with urethane foam and then glass over it. You can rent a sprayer and the bonding should be no big thing.

This method has one giant failing: it's impossible to spray on a smooth even coat of urethane, even for the most experienced craftsman. The result, at best, would be wartish to the extent where a solid week is required to bring the surface to a condition smooth enough for bonding over. The week would be spent at planing, curving, and grinding the foam, a dusty, itchy, miserably unrewarding task. Avoid it.

The remaining alternative is fitting and installing solid urethane foam sheets into cabinets. This procedure is no dream job either since you'll have to crawl into spaces you've previously considered too small for a dog and work often in very dim light with very little air. The foam can be cut with a knife. If the surface is large and curved, the foam should be sliced to allow small straight pieces to form the required arch. A few spots of tile cement will suffice to hold the pieces in place until bonding.

Since bonding over the foam is necessary to protect it, one must use urethane. Like styrene, urethane comes in sheets of varying thickness and, although it is more expensive than styrene, it has two advantages. First, it is a 30 percent better insulator. Second, it will not melt when used in conjunction with polyester resin. It is usually green or tan in color, is very brittle, and is much itchier than styrene but you have to use it.

Because it is almost impossible to measure and cut large accurate pieces of mat to fit over the odd curves and angles of a cabinet's belly, I used 6″ mat tape (the same that I used for bonding plywood to hull). A single layer of ounce and a half mat (with edges overlapped an inch) proved sufficient after numerous stress tests. The tests were quite basic, involving little more than dropping a quite ordinary hammer from assorted heights. If you can devise more profound testing, proceed.

One noteworthy point. When you are putting in the foam, leave a 2″ gap between its upper edge and whatever plywood surface you have above it. When you bond over the foam, finish off the bond only onto the hull and not onto the plywood. We had made the mistake of doing the opposite. When water found its way onto the horizontal plywood surface, it ran behind the bond and into the sealed pocket formed by the lower bond. We didn't discover this mistake until installing a transducer. I was drilling from outside the hull, waiting to see light, only to be showered by brown stale water. We ended up tearing part of the insulation out and rebonding the whole cabinet. So beware.

Perhaps a few inconspicuous drain holes through the bottom of the bond would not be overcautious, but try to be sure that you don't drill through your hull. In bonding, do as clean a job as possible, leaving no hard strands or upturned ends.

Once bonded, paint over all surfaces, first with a coat of undercoat (Z-Spar 105 or equivalent) then with one or two coats of easy-to-clean gloss or semigloss enamel. It's best to get mildew-proof paint. Although manufacturers' of marine paints insist that their product exceeds all others in quality and wonderfulness, I have been reassured by those who know that paint is paint is paint. So use almost any exterior mildew-proof oil base. The cheaper the better.

Soft Urethane Foam

Some people advocate the use of soft urethane foam (like cushion) with a vinyl cover, contact-cemented to the hull. I think that it is quite satisfactory under a wood cover, but I cannot see how a clean tidy fit can be achieved inside cabinets, for the shapes created by compound curves are almost unimaginable. Apart from aesthetics, if heavy objects such as cans and tools are to be stored, the soft foam will collapse to such an insignificant thickness that its insulative qualities will be decimated.

I do, however, believe that neoprene foam (preferably the non-flammable type) is ideal for soundproofing the engine room. This material represents an expensive venture, but diesels are annoyingly noisy; therefore it may be worthwhile. Thickness of up to 1½″ may be required to be effective (see "Engine Room Insulation").

BOAT CUSHIONS

Before we delve deeply into the construction aspects of boat cushions, let us get a few things into perspective.

As far as I can make out, most of us spend hundreds of dollars on various upholstery materials to cover up our foam mattresses because we consider them: a) unpleasant to sit on, and b) ugly. Now the point that needs clarification is why so many people choose materials that possess the above two qualities to an even greater extent than the thing which they're trying to cover up.

The smooth vinyl upholstery is admittedly very easy to keep clean and will resist most spilled things, but it also repels most humans. It has a general tactility that rivals the skin of a just-dead toad; in cold weather, it's at least $50°$ colder than the surrounding air; and in hot weather, it will quickly generate such quantities of moisture in one's lower garments that it will make the wettest diaper of one's memories seem like a patch of the Sahara desert.

Then, of course, we have the woven polyesters, which usually do their utmost to imitate old Irish weaving, but are betrayed by their crisp, shiny fibres which have the texture delicacy of an average Brillo pad.

Long forgotten by most, but still clinging tenaciously to last century's furniture, and just begging you to come close and touch and stroke and cuddle, is beautiful, delicate, as soft and soothing as a mother's breast; cotton.

It comes in the world's most beautiful natural colours, and it looks fresh and new year after year, and I was told by the proprietor of the finest furniture store in Newport that it will outlast, and outwear, any Shinyester or Jerkulon material, and that's a lot to say because cotton cushions are forever sat on, fondled, and used.

We've had raw cotton cushions on *Warm Rain* for over three years. She was our full-time home for at least half of that time, and all our cushions still look brand new even after washings, even after cups of spilled tea and a whole bowl of fish soup.

The choice in good upholstery cotton, with rubber backing that keeps it from sliding and stretching, is limitless. It ranges from corduroys and gabardine to the most elegant velvets and brocades. They are, of course, fairly pricey, but so is a Mercedes Benz. You get what you pay for.

Foam

Good quality polyurethane foam seems to be the best choice for cushions of a yacht. Foam rubber breaks down in the heat, absorbs

THE FINELY FITTED YACHT

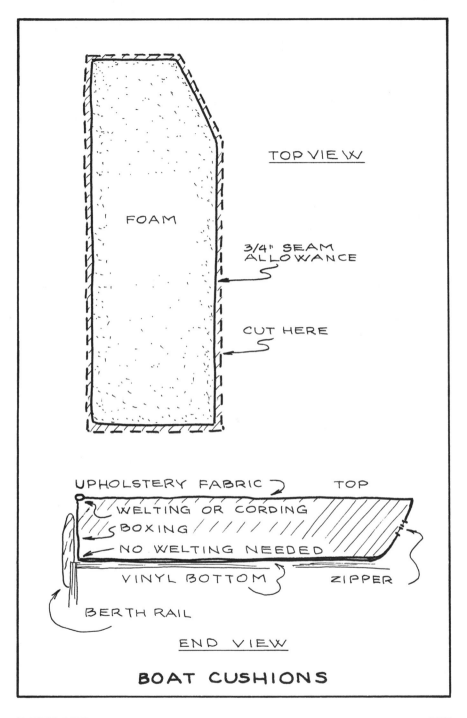

TOP VIEW

FOAM

3/4" SEAM ALLOWANCE

CUT HERE

UPHOLSTERY FABRIC   TOP

WELTING OR CORDING

BOXING

NO WELTING NEEDED

VINYL BOTTOM   ZIPPER

BERTH RAIL

END VIEW

BOAT CUSHIONS

water insatiably, and develops a rather strange odour in time. But it does retain its firmness better than the poly.

A good foam person will describe to you the best type (in terms of firmness) to get, depending on your personal tastes. Do beware when you are choosing. I once made the mistake of purchasing a 4″ foam mattress that was actually harder than the plywood berth it was on. A good solution if you want a firm mattress, but no bruises in the morning, may be to select, for a 4″ overall thickness, 3″ of very firm foam, and have the foam person glue on top of it 1″ of medium firm foam. You will then have the initial welcoming softness without the "bottoming out" that's such a frequent occurrence on the less firm foams.

Liners

Since, because of their limiting shapes, very few yacht cushions can be turned bottom up and used, the undersides of cushions should be made of vinyl. Mildew and stains are easy to remove from it and, of course, it will cost considerably less than the velvet or the corduroy.

Threads, Zippers, and Welting

The best all round thread is polyester, mostly because it will not be weakened by mildew as a cotton thread may. Zippers are costly critters, especially if you buy them made to length. Delrin (plastic) zippers are available on rolls by the yard, and if you have a whole boat of cushions to do, you may as well buy them as such, cut them to length, and slip the sides on yourself. This way if you make a mistake on your cushion, you will not have to fix and patch; you can simply make your zipper shorter or longer than planned. The plastic zipper doesn't bind as easily as its metal counterpart and, of course, it won't rust.

To calculate the length of the zipper per cushion, measure the back of each cushion and subtract between two and five inches, but no more. If the zipper is too short, getting the foam back into that envelope will be like wrestling with an alligator.

The welting is the thin sausage that circumvents the upper joints (side to top) of cushion covers. It helps to hide stitch irregularities and adds firmness to seams as well. It is actually made up of a cord or a nylon worm sewn into a tube of the upholstery material which is then, in turn, sewn to each of the pieces it borders. The material for welts should be cut on a bias (45° to the weave) if the material lacks rubberized backing. This is to avoid fraying. On material with a

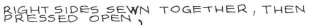

RIGHT SIDES SEWN TOGETHER, THEN
PRESSED OPEN

ZIPPER STITCHED
RIGHT SIDE DOWN

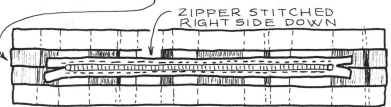

ZIPPER   INSTALLATION

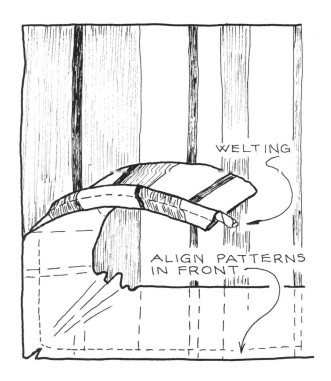

WELTING

ALIGN PATTERNS
IN FRONT

STITCHING SIDES TO TOP

BOAT CUSHIONS

backing, this precaution can be bypassed and the welting can be cut to a width of 1″-1½″ (with the usual 1/8″ diameter nylon worm) from a single strip of fabric.

Construction

Patterning

For anything but a completely regular cushion, you should make a pattern out of brown paper. If you're simply recovering an existing cushion, just use the foam as your pattern piece.

Next, lay the fabric "wrong" side up (that's a sewing term for the side you don't want to see) and lay your foam or paper pattern over it, and outline the shape with tailor's chalk. If you use a felt pen or a ballpoint, the ink will bleed through the first time the cushion gets wet. Outside the line you've just drawn, draw another one from 3/4″ to 1″ away. This will be for what is known in sewing as *seam allowance*. The generous width will absorb any cutting mistakes.

Cut along the seam allowance, and label the pieces with tailor's chalk. Mark all your pieces as you lay them out, not only with their name, but also with specific references, like "forward edge," "top edge," etc. Now, cut the long and short side pieces (known as *boxing*). It's always advisable to use the factory-finished edges, for then you'll have at least one true edge per piece. Don't forget the 3/4″ seam allowance on *each* side (all four) of every piece (see diagram).

When laying out the sides, it's advantageous to cut the entire run (all the way around), except for the zippered end, as a single piece. This will save you two extra seams. One word of caution. When pinning the sides to the top, be sure you align the pattern at the front (visible) side of the cushion; the hidden sides be damned. The zippered side will be the same width as the other sides plus one inch, cut horizontally in half. The "right" sides of this zippered end are then sewn together, allowing for a 1/2″ seam, at the ends where the zipper will terminate. Open up the material, iron the seams flat, and lay the zipper, right side down, in the centre of the seams. Baste it in place, then stitch it. You'll be going through three layers, so don't rush the machine.

Next, lay out the bottom of the cushion on coated vinyl and mark and cut as you did the top.

Finally, in the cutting department, cut sufficient lengths of welting material (the house for the worm) to a width of 2″, as you will need to run all around the seams where the top joins the sides.

Since the lower edges of most cushions are hidden by searails, this welting hocus-pocus can be bypassed there.

Sewing

The sewing should be done in the following order: (a) cord to welting, (b) welting to side, (c) zipper into side, (d) side to top, (e) side to bottom. Some sewing books advocate the melting of (a) and (b) together to eliminate one step. Whichever way you choose, lay the cord into the centre of the welt strip and fold the strip so the two edges match. With the zipper or cord foot on your machine, sew along the welting strip as close to the cord as possible. Leave the last 2″ unfinished so the ends of the welts can be mated.

To attach the sides (boxing) to the top, pin the boxing to the *centre* of the top cover front edge, then proceed with the pinning away from the centre and around the corners. If you find that your zipper will be a touch off centre in the back, don't worry about it, worse things have happened. Take care to put equal tension on the top and the boxing, and smooth both equally, or you will end up sewing in permanent wrinkles. To make the cover a nice tight fit, cheat on your pinning and reduce the top piece by 1/4″ all around.

Now, turn the pieces inside out and sew them together, running the needle as close to the cord as possible. Sew in the bottom in similar fashion.

Turn the covers right side out, and take your foam and stuff it.

DETAILING

At the joyous moment when the completion of your project flutters just above your fingertips, you will be faced with the grandpop of all icebergs. Somehow, somewhere, someone christened this horribly fidgety, monstrously time-consuming, and penuriously rewarding task, "detailing." This cultured term refers to resanding, repainting, regelcoating, recleaning, and generally rebuilding the entire thing you've just built.

At any rate, there are a few short cuts and precautions which can be pursued to achieve a completely satisfactory job in minimum time. The greatest time saver, of course, is sufficient preparation and careful rough assembly. If you did the job well, the task now facing you will be minimal.

Painting

It seems, through practice, that short grain woods, like mahogany, make for a better surface than wider grained ones like fir. Though you may be considering covering plywood cabinetry with paint, it may well be worth the extra two dollars per 4 X 8 foot sheet to use mahogany plywood instead of fir. You may argue that with dedicated sanding the fir can be brought to just as fine a finish. Quite the contrary. The more you sand, the deeper will be the softer grains and the more highlighted the more pitchy, harder ones.

One solution that does improve fir is painting the wood while still unsanded with a coat of undercoat, then sanding, then painting, then sanding, etc. By this process, the softer grained areas will be protected by semi-hard covering. I had to use this method on one piece of fir plywood that I recklessly substituted for mahogany. Not only did sanding take an unimaginably long time, but it possessed the added featurette of covering the minutest surface with a thorough coating of white dust that lifted and thickened the air every time I blinked. So try to use mahogany; if you can't, suffer.

Your painting chores will be much easier if you mask unpainted adjoining areas with tape. This practice is admittedly time-devouring, but not nearly as bad as scraping blobs of paint from wood. Since the paint will penetrate into most woods (the drier the deeper) overslop could lead to major problems. To get out all the unwanted paint, you will need to carve irreparable gulleys with sandpaper. In solid wood, such repairs are less noticeable than on plywood. On plywood, very slight over-zealousness can result in your penetrating the thin (with teak plywood only one mil thick) top layer of veneer. I have not yet heard of a satisfactory method of veneer repair.

So tape off the perimeter of your areas and you will save hours of frustration. To help even further, seal off the area adjacent to the masking tape with a clear wood sealer and acid brush. This procedure should prevent any paint from seeping under the tape. If it does not, at least the paint will not penetrate the sealed wood and it will be easy to remove.

On the painted surface, use a quick drying undercoat. Z-Spar 105 is very satisfactory, although I'm not convinced that other oil-based undercoats perform any less commendably. Even if you use mahogany ply, it is a good idea to sand well between coats. The first undercoat will be almost completely removed if you want a good job. Brush strokes are left by the finest brushes; if left unsanded, they will become more accentuated with each following coat. I'm not advocating a formica-like finish, but a soft smooth finish will bring hours of pleasure in silent dawning light.

Although Z-Spar 105 is a wonderful undercoat, I cannot recommend Z-Spar products for subsequent layers. Their finishing paint is very thick (I'm told that a good finish paint should be no thicker than fresh milk) resulting in a multitude of runs and brush marks. Apart from this problem, it has the irritating habit of never drying, thus clogging up a four-cent quarter-piece of sandpaper on the first stroke.

Interlux makes excellent finishing paints in many beautiful quick-drying shades. It also is difficult to sand, not because it fills the sandpaper, but for quite the opposite reason. It has a very hard protective finish.

A good rule is to use two undercoats (as mentioned) and two finishing coats. Some people advocate four or five finishing coats, but then some people mow their front lawn five times a week. After the last coat of paint has dried, don't leap to tear off the masking tape. If you do, you'll tear half the paint with it. Some paint will have overflown on to the tape and you will find a tendency for this overflow to pull the other paint with it instead of breaking conscientiously where the tape ends. To avoid pulling off paint take a sharp knife and literally cut the paint around the tape's edge. You can then pull the tape off cleanly and admire your masterpiece.

Masking tape will come in handy during procedures other than painting. If you are sanding a surface which is at right angles to another, you will be endlessly either hand sanding grooves into the other surface, or gouging it repeatedly while you use a vibrator or belt sander. To avoid the unnecessary repairs that will have to follow, tape the edge of the surface you won't be sanding, the wider the tape the better. WARNING — As exceptionally beneficial as masking tape is, it does have one villainous quality. If left on over a long period in a place where direct sunlight hits it, the glue will penetrate the surface it's on and cling tenaciously while the paper backing will crumble in your hands. We once left a strip of tape all around the fiberglass bulwarks when we caulked our teak decks. Absurd as it may seem, Candace and I spent 18 tearful hours scraping off 64 feet of one-inch wide tape. It was about as much fun as practice bleeding.

Sanding

If you are sanding wood, no matter how solid and thick it is, use sandpaper of no rougher grit than 60. You can still shape wood rapidly with 60 grit, if necessary. Any rougher grit will leave deep gouges (especially if you are going cross-grain) which will be very difficult to remove. Cross-grain sanding should be avoided if at all possible. On exterior surfaces, I can see no need to go finer than 150 at the most. If you are oiling exterior teak, to go finer than that is a waste, because the grain of the wood will rise drastically within two or three days no matter whom you know. If you are varnishing, you may consider going to 220 on your last run on the wood, but then varnish immediately because the grain will rise as soon as the dew falls. Two hundred twenty is acceptable to use between coats, although some say to use 400 before your last coat.

If you can afford to (and you almost can't afford not to), buy sandpaper by the sleeve. A sleeve usually contains 50 or 100 sheets. It is cheaper and you will end up using it all, especially common grits like 80, 100, and 150.

On interiors, you may consider using 220 on all your woods. If you are varnishing,you will need to; and if you are oiling, you may as well for then you can oil the wood and immediately run over it with 600 grit to achieve a nearly hand-rubbed finish.

Oiling

The only important point here is to wipe down the wood with an acetone dampened cloth before oiling. Keep turning the cloth to get all of the sawdust out of the grain. If you don't, it will have a tendency to darken once the oil is applied, rendering the wood lifeless and dark.

The first coat of oil you apply should be of a resin type, like Watco Interior Danish teak oil. It does have a pungent odour, but it seals and protects wood better than wood sealers. Later coats can be of resinless variety, like lemon oil.

Be sure to wipe all excess oil (that which has not absorbed) no more than 20 minutes after application. If you don't, it will become tacky and attract every speck of dust and fluff as well as make the surface unsightly with patches of unequal sheen.

For the exterior, use oil recommended for that purpose only. Watco makes one that has a tendency to turn grey and unappealingly black within a very few weeks. Others, like Tip-Top Teak Oil, blacken to a lesser extent. Light sanding is highly recommended before a new coat of exterior oil is applied. A very fine product called "Te-Ka" cleans the wood better than sandpaper because it penetrates deeper. A very good idea after sanding a coat of varnish or a coat of oil, instead of using acetone which may be spilled and cause patches, would be to use a product by the name of "Tac-Cloth." It is a messy, toadish feeling cloth that is treated with a substance which absorbs fantastic quantities of dust from even the graniest woods.

Varnishing

As mentioned, you may want to prepare the surface with 220 grit sandpaper. Then, a thinned-down sealing layer (about 20-25% paint thinner) should be applied followed by light sanding, then a full strength varnish coat. It is a fallacy that each coat has to be sanded to the point where no hairline is left untouched. Unless you want a glasslike finish, light sanding will do nicely. Apply the varnish in thin coats. Five thin coats are better than three thick ones which may run and curdle when touched, even days after application. After sanding, wipe with a Tac-Cloth or similar product.

Be sure your varnish is applied at least three hours before the dew falls, if you are doing exterior wood. In climates where the day may have been cooler than 60 degrees, try to have your varnishing finished by mid-morning or the dew will ruin your precious work. For the eccentrics it might be a great matter of pride to use refrigerated varnish. Varnish, thus cooled, will have a tendency to dry "from the inside out" and consequently have a better hold. I was told this by an eccentric and I never did quite figure out what he meant, but it might be worth a try.

Do not be frugal. Buy a good quality brush and clean it meticulously after using. There's nothing worse than picking molting hairs or kernels of hardened varnish from your otherwise perfect surface.

Filling

Small marks which are deep or irreparable can be drilled and plugged. A teak or mahogany plug out of place does not look as bad as a worm hole or a blob of white paint or a deep gouge. If the spot is large, patching could be considered. Patching is nothing more than the old art of inlaying wood. If you have a bad area, chisel it out very carefully and fill it with a piece of wood. If the grains match perfectly, that's wonderful. If they don't match at all, it looks good, and if you use entirely different kinds of wood, it looks even more intentional. Whichever you use, cut your filler piece to size first, then use it as a pattern on the damaged wood to scribe in the perimeter, then chisel out the damaged piece. Use a very sharp cutting tool or you will cause more damage through chipping than what you set out to repair to begin with. Keep a wetting stone handy.

If you suffer long splits in wood like we did with our hatches, the repair is simple. Many people use just glue or glue mixed with sawdust. I find either solution most unsatisfactory. You will end up with very dark coloured seams or cracks which probably look worse than the crack itself. The best way to fill cracks in wood is to use wood. Cut long wedges, cover the sides with glue and drive them into the cracks with a mallet. Then chisel and sand off the remaining bulk.

If you pick your wood colour to match, the inserted wedges will be unnoticeable.

Gelcoat Touch-Up

If chips in the gelcoat occur, follow this procedure:
— Clean the area with acetone.
— Fill the crack with body putty.
— Sand with 400 grit sandpaper.
— Spray on gelcoat.
— Spray on sealer.
— Peel off the tape before the gelcoat hardens.
— Wash off sealer with water.
— After it has gone off, sand the whole area with 600 grit. If you don't do your final sanding immediately following the catalyzation of the gelcoat, you may run into another problem, especially if you had taped off the area round which you sprayed. Very likely you will have a sharp edge of fresh gelcoat protruding which, if not feathered in immediately, may result in chipping. So sand with 600 grit and feather in.

Other Problems

If you do have stubborn problems with over-cooked masking tape or polyethylene which the sun baked onto your mast, deck, or caprail, only one economical remedy seems possible. People have attempted to use acetone, thinners, heat guns, and fingernails to no avail. The only thing that seems to work is steam cleaning. You can rent portable units or find companies which will come out to your aid. If your mistake is portable (like a boom), take it to the nearest do-it-yourself car wash and do-it-yourself.

LIST OF SUPPLIERS

CATALOGS

Spyglass
2415 Mariner Square Drive
Alameda, CA 94501
> *The* Spyglass *catalogue is actually a very beautifully produced reference volume, edited by a most gracious gentleman by the name of Dick Moore. The contents depart from standard catalogue fare with many articles and outfitting tips, aside from the few hundred pages of all marine gear imaginable.*

Thomas Foulkes
Landsdown Road, Leytonstone
London, England, E11 3HB
> *This has been the bible of cruising boat outfitters for many years. The catalogues normally run about 200 pages and cost about $10, but are well worth the price.*

Lands' End Catalog
2317 N. Elston
Chicago, IL 60614

Mariners Catalog
National Fisherman and International
Marine Publishing Co.
Camden, ME

James Bliss Co.
Dedham, MA 02026

Manhattan Marine
116 Chambers Street
New York, NY 10007

Jay Stuart Haft
8925 N. Tennyson Dr.
Milwaukee, WI 53217

THE FINELY FITTED YACHT

SPARS

Le Fiel
Mast and rigging, aluminum
13700 Firestone Blvd.
Santa Fe Springs, CA 90670

Shepperd Woodworks
Wood spars
21020 70th West
Edmonds, WA 98020

Super Spar
Masts, aluminum
7231 Rosecrans Ave.
Paramount, CA 90723

Forespar
Spars and fittings
3140 Pullman St.
Costa Mesa, CA 92627

Metal Mast Marine
Aluminum spars and related fittings
P.O. Box 471
Putnam, CT 06260

Sparcraft
Masts and assorted hardware
P.O. Box 925, 770 W. 17th St.
Costa Mesa, CA 92627

Forespar, Inc.
Rigging and spinnaker poles
3140 Pullman St.
Costa Mesa, CA 92626

WOOD

American Forest Products
All hardwoods and marine plywood
14103 Park Place
Cerritos, CA 90701

American Hardwood
1900 E. 15th St.
Los Angeles, CA 90021

Rogers Woodworking
Custom marine woodwork
874 W. 18th St.
Costa Mesa, CA 92627

Albano Marine Woodwork
Custom wood parts
% Wave Traders
1702 Bridgeway
Sausalito, CA 94965

H & L Woodwork
2965 E. Harcourt St.
Compton, CA 90221

The Harbor Sales Co.
Marine plywoods
1401 Russell St.
Baltimore, MD 21230

Penberthy
5800 S. Boyle Ave.
Los Angeles, CA 90058

RIGGING

Forespar
3140 Pullman St.
Costa Mesa, CA 92627

Hood Industries Rigging
951 Newhall St.
Costa Mesa, CA 92627

Ronstan (Alexander Roberts)
Running rigging
1851 Langley Ave.
Irvine, CA 92705

Universal Wire Products, Inc.
Rigging
222 Universal Drive
North Haven, CT 06473

DECK HARDWARE

American Precision Marine
Deck hardware
1260 Montauk Highway E.
Patachoque, NY 11772

Barient
Winches, etc.
936 Bransten Road
San Carlos, CA 94070

Barlow Winches
Alexander Roberts Co.
1851 Langley Ave.
Irvine, CA 92705

Clamcleat
Sneve-Nysether Co.
Box 1201
Everett, WA 98206

Gibb
Winches, turnbuckles, hardware, Hasler vang gear
82 Border St.
Cohasset, MD 02025

Harken
Blocks
1251 E. Wisconsin Ave.
Pewaukee, WI 53072

Hye
Deck gear
1075 Shell Blvd., #12
Foster City, CA 94404

Johnson Yacht Hardware
Lifeline hardware
Main Street
Middle Haddam, CT 06456

Lewmar Marine Yacht Hardware
Winches and rigging hardware
892 W. 18th St.
Costa Mesa, CA 92627

Merriman Holbrook
Complete line of deck hardware including winches
301 River St.
Grand River, OH 44045

Navtec Inc.
Rigging hardware
P.O. Box 277, Maynard Industrial Park
Maynard, MA 01754

Nicro-Fico
Complete line of hardware for running rigging
2065 N. Ave 140th
San Leandro, CA 94577

Ronstan (Alexander Roberts)
1851 Langley Ave.
Irvine, CA 92705

Schaeffer Marine
Complete line of deck and running rigging hardware
Industrial Park
New Bedford, MA 02745

Wilcox-Crittendon
Complete line of marine hardware
Middletown, CT 06457

GENERAL HARDWARE

Harding Machine Marine Parts
Individual custom hardware
1733 Monrovia Ave., Suite N
Costa Mesa, CA 92627

Harris Marine
Individual custom hardware
1281 Logan
Costa Mesa, CA 92626

Vic Berry
Best fuel and water tanks in the whole world
760 Newton Way
Costa Mesa, CA 92627

R.C. Plath Co.
Bronze hardware and anchor windlasses
337 N.E. 10th Ave.
Portland, OR 97232

Caseco
All types stainless steel fasteners
1215 S. State College Blvd.
Fullerton, CA 92631

Moritz Foundry
Windlass and other beautiful bronze cast marine hardware
133 Industrial Way
Costa Mesa, CA 92627

Beckson Manufacturing
Pumps, vents, hatches, etc.
Box 3336
Bridgeport, CT 06605

Danforth
Anchors, compasses, instruments
500 Riverside Industrial Parkway
Portland, ME 04013

Mariner Yacht Hardware
Blocks, deck hardware
1714 Seventeenth
Santa Monica, CA 90404

Nicro-Fico
Complete line of hardware for running rigging
2065 W. Ave 140th
San Leandro, CA 94577

PYHI
ABS plastic portlights and vents
1647 N. Avalon Blvd.
Wilmington, CA 90744

Rostand, Inc.
Ecclesiastical brass and marine hardware
Milford, CT 06460

Seagull Marine
Avon, Whale pumps, CQR anchors and Simpson Lawrence
Windlass and British hardware
1851 McGaw Ave.
Irvine, CA 92705

Wilcox-Crittendon
Complete line of marine hardware
Middleton, CT 06457

Yacht Specialties Co., Inc.
Wheel steering
15 5 E. St. Gertrude Place
Santa Ana, CA 92705

Bomar Company
Hatches
1021 E. State St.
Westport, CT 06880

ELECTRONICS

Dawn Electronics Corp.
Knotmeter and taffrail log
P.O. Box 91736
Los Angeles, CA 90009

Davis Instruments
Navigation supplies
857 Thornton St.
San Leandro, CA 94577

Fisheries Supply
Everything
Pier 55
Seattle, WA 98101

Kenyon Marine
Navigation instruments, hardware
New Whitfield St.
Guilford, CT 06437

Ray Jefferson
Radios, electronics, instruments
Main & Cotton St.
Philadelphia, PA 19127

Signet Scientific Comp.
Yacht instruments
129 E. Tujunga Ave., P.O. Box 6489
Burbank, CA 91510

Telcor Instruments Inc.
Yacht instruments
17785 Sky Park Circle, Box CC
Irvine, CA 02664

VDO Instruments
Knotmeters
116 Victor
Detroit, MI 48203

GENERAL

Ferro Corp.
All fiberglass materials
18811 Fiberglass Road
Huntington Beach, CA 92648

Detco Grove
Two part polysulfide caulking for teak decks
3452 East Foothill Blvd.
Pasadena, CA 91107

Larwyck Development
Windvanes
17330 Raymer St.
Northridge, CA

Dickinson Marine
Diesel stoves and heaters
#103 4241 21st Ave. West
Seattle, WA 98199

Marine Vane Gears
Windvanes
Cowes, Isle of Wight
England

Alco Mining
Lead ballast casting
16908 S. Broadway
Gardena, CA

Norcold Inc.
Refrigerators
11121 Weddington
North Hollywood, CA 91601

Norton Products
Holding plate refrigeration systems
173-M Monrovia Ave.
Costa Mesa, CA 92627

Thalco Uniglas Co.
Fiberglass
1212 McGaw Ave.
Santa Ana, CA 92705

Boat Transit
Boat hauling cross-country
P.O. Box 1403
Newport Beach, CA 92663

Fatsco
Beautiful solid fuel ship's stoves
251 N. Fair Ave.
Benton Harbor, MI

Lavender Fasteners
All stainless steel fasteners
884 W. 18th St.
Costa Mesa, CA 92627

Southwest Instruments
Navigation aids, marine supplies, books and everything you can dream of
235 W. 7th St.
San Pedro, CA

Aquadron/Acme
First aid kits
1113 Johnston Building
Charlotte, NC 28281

Atlantis
Foul weather gear
Waitsfield, VT 05673

Canor Plarex
Foul weather gear
4200 23rd Ave. W.
Seattle, WA 98199

Aonolite
Reinforced fiberglass foam
425 Maple Ave.
Carpentersville, IL 60110

Doris Hammond
Canvas bags
260 Kearny St.
San Francisco, CA 94108

Edson
Steering equipment
480 E. Industrial Park Road
New Bedford, MA 02745

Guest
Yacht lights
17 Culbro Drive
West Hartford, CT 06110

Interlux Paints
Marine finishes
220 S. Linden Ave.
So. San Francisco, CA 94080

A.B. Optimus
Stoves and lanterns
P.O. Box 907, 1251 Beach Blvd.
La Habra, CA 90631

Paul Luke Inc.
Stoves and cabin heater
East Boothbay, ME 04544

Sailrite Kits
Sail and awning kits
2010 Lincoln Blvd.
Venice, CA 90291

Samson Cordage Works
Dacron and nylon braided line
470 Atlantic Ave.
Boston, MA 02210

Z-Spar Koppers Co. Inc.
Marine finishes
1900 Koppers Building
Pittsburgh, PA 15219

Woolsey Marine Ind.
Marine finishes and winches
201 E. 42nd St.
New York, NY 10017

TOOLS

The following companies have some of the most beautiful tools imaginable. Their catalogues alone are a feast for the craftsman's eyes.

Brookstone
127 Vose Farm Road
Peterborough, NH 03458

Garrett Wade
302 Fifth Avenue
New York, NY 10001

Leichtung
701 Beta Dr. #17
Cleveland, OH 44143

Adjustable Clamp Co.
417 N. Ashland Ave.
Chicago, IL 60622

The Princeton Co.
P.O. Box 276
Princeton, MA

WOODWORKINGS

H&L Marine Woodworking Inc.
2965 E. Harcourt St.
Compton, CA 90221

> *H&L is the major North American source of prefabricated teak or mahogany wood workings Their range spans from the simplest flag pole, through items like towel racks, doors, drawers, magazine racks, book racks, etc. They will also custom fabricate hatches, cockpit grates and swimsteps to your specifications. Their work is usually of very good quality and their prices are most reasonable. A number of ideas in this volume were taken from their products.*

GLOSSARY OF TERMS

— A —

Acetone — A very combustible, fast evaporating, fluid used for cleaning surfaces. The only thing that will dissolve and clean polyester resin.

Arbour — An attachment used with a drill motor; supports hole saws of different sizes. Usually has a drill bit inserted through its center.

— B —

Back-Up Plates — Reinforcing plates, usually steel or brass, used when bolting through vulnerable material such as wood or fiberglass.

Bedlog — A set of raised tracks upon which the main hatch slides.

Bevel — The act of cutting to a taper.

Bevel Square — An adjustable tool which, with two arms and a wingnut, can be used to duplicate or record angles.

Bolt Rope — Roping around the edge of a sail or awning, needed to distribute the strain on the cloth.

Bull-Nose — (A) to round off a sharp edge; (B) a concave bladed router bit used to round off a sharp edge; (C) the rounded edge itself.

Butt Connector — A metal press fitting that unites two wires end to end without complex splicing.

— C —

Cap Nut — A finishing nut with one side sealed off.

Carriage Bolt — A smooth-headed bolt with squared shoulders to keep it from turning.

THE FINELY FITTED YACHT

Center Punch — A pointed tool for making marks on wood or metal.

Cleat Stock — Square cross-sectioned strips of wood used to join perpendicularly uniting pieces of plywood.

Countersink — To set the head of a screw or bolt below the surface; tool used for this purpose.

— D —

Deck Beams — Athwartship beams that support the deck.

Dolfinite — A very oily bedding compound best used on fiberglass to wood, or wood to wood joints.

Dovetailing — A very positive method of corner joints for wood, using intermeshing wedge shapes for each piece as fasteners.

Dovetail Saw — A very stiff-bladed hand saw with a well reinforced blade for very accurate cutting.

Dowels — Wood turnings used as a common attachment, usually to join boards edge to edge.

— E —

Elbow Catch — A spring loaded catch for cabinet doors, usually hidden and accessible through a finger hole.

Epoxy Glue and Resin — A high strength synthetic adhesive that will stick anything to anything.

Eye — A closed loop, in wire-rope or line.

— F —

Feather — To even two adjoining levels into each other.

Flare — To widen or ream the end of a pipe for coupling purposes.

Flathead — A bevel-shouldered screw.

Gelcoat — A very hard outer coating (usually color pigmented) of a fiberglass boat.

Grommet — A brass eye sewn or pressed into canvas work.

− H −

Hack Saw — A very fine tooth bladed saw (the blade is removable) made for metal cutting.

Hatch Coaming — Built up buffer around the inside of a hatch opening to keep out water intruding under the hatch.

Hole Saws — Circular, heavy walled saw blades of infinite diameters used in conjunction with a drill motor to cut holes.

Hose Barb — A tapered fitting, with terraced ridges that allow a hose to slip on but not off.

Hose Clamp — An adjustable stainless steel ring used to fasten hoses to fittings.

Hose Ties — Plastic ties with a barbed tongue and eye used to fasten hoses to bulkheads, sole, etc.

− I −

Inboard — Toward the centreline.

− K −

Key Hole Saw — A very narrow bladed hand saw with one end of the blade unsupported, used for hole or curve cutting.

− M −

Machine Screw — A fine threaded, slot headed fastener made to be used with a tapped hole.

Mat — An unwoven fiberglass material made up of randomly layered short fibres.

Miter Box — A wood or metal frame which is used with a hand saw to cut material at a given angle.

Miter Gauge — The sliding fitting on a table or band saw against which the piece of wood is laid to assure a straight cut. The gauge itself is adjustable to any angle required.

Molding — Trimming pieces of wood or plastic that hide joints or mistakes or both.

— O —

Oval Head — A screw with a head of that shape.

— P —

Pad Eye — A through bolted deck fitting to accommodate blocks, lines, etc.

Pet Cock — A small 90° turn off-on valve ideal for fuel switch.

Plastic Resin Glue — A powder base, mixed with water, that forms a very strong, water-resistant glue.

Plug — A tight fitting wood dowel used to fill screw-head holes.

Polysulfide — An unbelievably effective, totally waterproof sealing-bedding compound.

— R —

Rabbet — A groove cut in a plank.

Resorcinol Glue — A two-part, completely waterproof, glue.

— S —

Scribe — To reproduce the curve of a surface onto another surface by using a compass with pencil.

GLOSSARY   303

Sheet Metal Screw — Coarse treaded, self-tapping screw.

Shrink Tubes — Plastic tubing slipped over wire splices then shrunk by heat to seal the splice.

Silicone Seal — A quick drying non-hardening sealing compound.

Swedge — Method of attaching, by pressure, fittings onto a wire rope.

— T —

Thimble — A round or heart-shaped metal–eye chafe protector, around which rope can be seized.

— V —

Vented Loop — A bronze fitting with a valve that prevents siphoning of water into appliances below the waterline.